The World of
Birds

The World of
Birds
Over 300 Species

Michael Wright

METRO BOOKS
New York

METRO BOOKS
New York

An Imprint of Sterling Publishing Co., Inc.
1166 Avenue of the Americas
New York, NY 10036

ISBN: 978-1-4351-5859-7

For information about custom editions, special sales, and premium and corporate purchases,
please contact Sterling Special Sales at 800-805-5489 or specialsales@sterlingpublishing.com.

Manufactured in China

2 4 6 8 10 9 7 5 3

www.sterlingpublishing.com

Editorial and design by
Amber Books Ltd

Project Editor: James Bennett
Design: Stylus Design

PICTURE CREDITS
Popperfoto: 13

ARTWORK CREDITS
All artwork © 2003 by Istituto Geografico De Agostini, Novara SPA except the following:
Marshall Editions: 14, 15, 16, 17, 18, 30, 40, 42, 46, 49, 51, 56, 64, 68, 72, 78, 79, 80, 81, 83, 85, 87, 90, 95, 98, 99, 116,
122, 124, 126, 130, 131, 134, 158, 187, 198, 229, 230, 231, 233, 234, 239, 244, 245, 247, 250, 252, 260, 261, 269, 273,
280, 281, 283, 284, 286, 293, 294, 295, 296, 299
Mike Langman: 1, 2–3, 4, 5, 6–7, 8–9, 10–11, 12–13, 19, 23, 29, 57, 67, 75

CONTENTS

Introduction

Birds are enormously varied and endlessly fascinating. We see them constantly all around us, in most places in greater numbers than any other wild creatures. They fascinate us with their colours, behaviour and skills. We admire their ability to fly, even envying their freedom. We love to observe their family relationships, social structure and other aspects of behaviour – from a mother duck shepherding her ducklings to the massed migrations of vast flocks each spring and autumn and the way many birds stoutly defend their territory against others.

As a result, you can study and enjoy birds in many different ways. As a bird-spotter, or 'twitcher', you may simply be interested in how many different types you can spot, identify and tick off on a list. You may be enthralled by birds' territorial or courtship behaviour, in which case you could spend a whole lifetime studying just one species, or distinct type, of bird. You might want to record birds' songs and calls, or you could study the populations, or numbers of various bird types in a particular locality and perhaps, even as an amateur, do valuable scientific work on how changes in the environment or other factors affect birds. The possibilities are endless.

The purpose of this book is to introduce you to all the major types of birds, from all parts of the world and every type of environment – from oceans to deserts, from mountains to forests, from city parks and gardens to the frozen wastes of Antarctica. It is impossible in a book of this size – or even in a much bigger one – to cover every known type of bird, for there are at least 8000 distinct species and perhaps well over 9000; even scientists disagree on the exact number, but it is certainly more than twice the number of mammal species. We have selected 300 representatives that illustrate birds' enormous variety and geographical range, including examples of every important family (collection of related species) and from every continent on Earth.

They are not always the most familiar types (for one thing, what is familiar in one part of the world may be a great rarity or even never be seen in another), and this helps to emphasize birds' diversity. Each is illustrated in colour, while the 'data' panel at the foot of each page summarizes the important facts about that bird in a standard format. The general text in between focuses on various aspects of the bird or its life, for every type of bird is unique and fascinating in its own special way. We hope you enjoy finding out about them.

Above: An artist's reconstruction of Archaeopteryx, a primitive reptile-like bird known only from 150-million-year-old fossils; the feather colours are imaginary.

MAIN EXTERNAL PARTS OF A BIRD

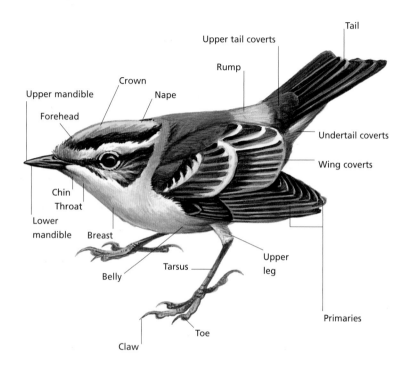

THE ORIGIN AND CHARACTERISTICS OF BIRDS

All birds have certain characteristics in common with other members of the animal kingdom, and certain features that are unique. Like mammals, they are warm-blooded – that is, they usually maintain their body temperature at a more or less constant level whatever the temperature of their surroundings. Like mammals, reptiles, amphibians and fish, they have a spine, or vertebral column – they are *vertebrates*. Like mammals, amphibians and most reptiles except snakes, they have four limbs, with the front ones (unlike in most other vertebrates) modified to form wings. Most (but not quite all) birds can fly – but so can bats, which are mammals, and many insects, which are not even vertebrates. Unlike any of these, however, birds' skin is covered with feathers rather than scales (as fish and reptiles have) or hair (like mammals). That is their unique characteristic.

Evidence from comparing birds' skeletons and other features with fossils lead scientists to believe that birds evolved from small, primitive dinosaurs. (In fact, the similarities are so clear that some experts say that the dinosaurs in effect never became extinct – birds are their surviving representatives!) The clearest single piece of evidence for the link between dinosaurs and birds is a fossil discovered in Germany in 1861. Given the scientific name *Archaeopteryx lithographica*, it has an obviously dinosaur-like skeleton and a long, lizard-like tail. Its front limbs are modified as wings, but also have claws, and it has teeth in its jaw, unlike modern birds. But clearly visible in the rock in which it was embedded is the impression, or mould, of feathers. These probably first evolved to keep the creature warm, just as the primitive mammals of the same period were evolving hair, but they also probably enabled it to fly well.

To this day, *Archaeopteryx* is the earliest known bird, about 150 million years old. Many later fossil birds are known, clearly showing how they evolved into the many modern types – especially quickly from the early part of the Tertiary period, which began about 65 million years ago. But so far no one has discovered an even earlier bird ancestor than *Archaeopteryx* – no 'missing link' to show even more clearly how dinosaurs evolved into birds.

ADAPTATIONS FOR FLIGHT

Despite the diversity of birds already mentioned, they are much more similar to each other than, say, mammals (which vary in size, weight and form from tiny bats and shrews to giant whales, many millions of times bigger and very different in shape). Even between the smallest hummingbird and the biggest ostrich the range is much smaller, and between hummingbirds and the biggest flying birds – which weigh about 15kg (33lb), although some fossil species were considerably larger – the difference is smaller still. The main reason is the adaptations – in weight and manoeuvrability – needed for efficient flight.

The most obvious of these adaptations is the development of wings and feathers. Feathers are extremely light but (at least the type found in birds' wings) very rigid, easily manoeuvred and shaped to form surfaces that provide lift as they move through the air. Much less obvious are the differences in a bird's skeleton. The skull is much lighter, with a much smaller jaw, than in other vertebrates; a lightweight but rigid bill – varying in shape according to the bird's normal diet – takes the place of the heavy jaw and teeth. Many bones are hollow, and the tail bones almost non-existent; the tail feathers all originate close together from the tail stump. The rib-cage is much stiffer than in other vertebrates, and in flying birds the breastbone is greatly enlarged to form a 'keel' to anchor the flight muscles.

Even less obvious are adaptations in the respiratory (breathing) system. This includes air sacs, to and from which air is pumped – via the lungs – when the bird breathes. As a result, air passes *through* the lungs, not just in and out of them, so that the bird obtains oxygen and gets rid of carbon dioxide far more efficiently than in mammals and other air-breathing creatures. This system enables some birds to fly as high as the highest mountains, and provides enough oxygen for hummingbirds, for example, to 'burn' food energy at a far faster rate, in relation to their size, than other animals; as a result they can beat their wings at an incredibly fast rate (*see pp.174–179*).

Birds' digestive systems are also adapted for flight, and for survival. The lightweight bill is of little use for grinding food; instead, the stomach has a muscular sac, the gizzard, where food is broken up. In some cases – especially grain-eaters – this is aided by swallowed grit. Many birds also have a temporary food-storage sac, growing from the side of the oesophagus (gullet), called the crop; this enables them to consume a lot of food quickly, then digest it at leisure, in a safe roost. Birds are also adapted to low water consumption, both to reduce flight weight and to shorten the time needed for drinking, when they are more vulnerable to predators. They get much of their water from their food, re-absorb much of it from their gut, and instead of producing urine expel wastes mostly in semi-solid form with their faeces. (They have a single opening for expelling waste, the cloaca, combining the function of the anus and urethra.)

MOULTING

Feathers become damaged and wear out, and birds replace them regularly – usually once a year and often after the breeding season. This is called moulting. Some birds moult all their feathers at once, and cannot fly (or, in the case of penguins, swim) for a few weeks while the new feathers grow (and, in penguins, become fully waterproof). In others, wing feathers are replaced progressively, and the bird can still fly – although not so well – while moulting takes place. In many species, the new feathers result in a different overall colour or pattern at different times of year – hence the terms 'breeding plumage' and 'winter plumage'.

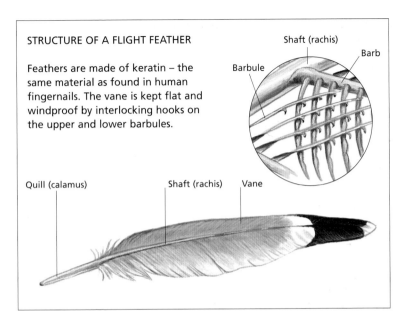

STRUCTURE OF A FLIGHT FEATHER

Shaft (rachis)

Barb

Barbule

Feathers are made of keratin – the same material as found in human fingernails. The vane is kept flat and windproof by interlocking hooks on the upper and lower barbules.

Quill (calamus)   Shaft (rachis)   Vane

Even in their method of reproduction, birds save body weight. All, without exception, lay eggs, whereas virtually all mammals and even some reptiles and fish bear live young – which, although protected more safely than eggs, obviously add to the mother's weight.

THE VARIETY AND CLASSIFICATION OF BIRDS

As they evolved, birds adapted to the enormous variety of environments and habitats they found themselves inhabiting, in particular specializing in exploiting particular sources of food – ranging from seeds and fruits to insects and the flesh of live and dead animals. (For examples of birds evolving in this way in an isolated area and a relatively short time, see the articles on Darwin's medium ground finch [*p.270*] and the iiwi [*p.279*].) Detailed studies of birds' anatomy, and also their patterns of behaviour, have enabled scientists to work out their probable evolutionary relationships – that is, which birds are most closely related to each other, in what way, and how they evolved.

Based on such studies, ornithologists (biologists who specialize in birds) have organized them into various groupings. The basic category is the *species* – a

MAJOR INTERNAL ORGANS OF A BIRD

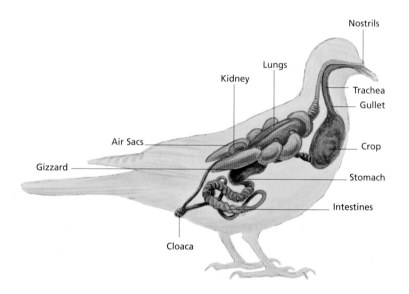

distinct type of bird which normally breeds only with other members of the same species. Many species are subdivided into *subspecies* and/or *races*, which show minor variations and often inhabit a particular part of the bird's range (the areas of the world in which it lives). For example, birds of a certain species living on the edge of the arctic may be paler in colour than those living farther south. However, not all ornithologists agree on how particular birds should be classified into species and subspecies – hence disagreements about how many species of birds there are.

A group of closely related species form a *genus* (plural *genera*), although sometimes a genus contains only one species. In the scientific (Latin) name, the genus name comes first, followed by the species name. For example, in the case of the ostrich, *Struthio camelus*, *Struthio* is the genus name, *camelus* the species name; you need to give both names to be precise about which bird you are referring to. When an article refers to two or more species of the same genus, the genus name is abbreviated (for example, *S. camelus*) after the first time it is mentioned. Genus, species and subspecies names are printed in italics.

There are also bigger classifications. One, two or more genera may be grouped to form a *family*, whose name always ends in '...idae'; for example, Corvidae is the crow family, which includes jays, magpies and other related birds. One, two or more families together form an *order*, whose name ends '...iformes'; the order appears at the very top of each page, above the common (ordinary English) name of the bird. Family and order names are not in italics.

Since the late 20th century, ornithologists have been able to use detailed studies of DNA (the genetic material found in all living cells) to show much more accurately than anatomical studies the evolutionary relationships between species – and particularly between families and orders – of birds. As a result, some have suggested significant changes to the classification of many groups; however, in general, this book keeps to the more familiar traditional groupings while pointing out important alternatives.

*Above: A blue-footed booby (*Sula nebouxii*), a fearless and rather stupid-looking member of the gannet family that lives on isolated islands of the eastern Pacific.*

Ostrich

The ostrich is not only the tallest living bird, with the biggest eggs, but also the fastest runner, reaching up to about 90km/h (55mph) in short bursts and 50km/h (30mph) for longer periods. But like other birds in the ratite group – including rheas, cassowaries, emus and kiwis – it cannot fly. The reason is that ratites have no keel (a flange-like extension) on the breastbone, to which the pectoral (chest) muscles of other birds are attached; these muscles power the wings. Ostriches live in large groups. A dominant male will have several mates but shares nesting duties with only one favoured female. Ostriches are farmed for their meat and feathers.

Scientific name	*Struthio camelus*
Family	Struthionidae
Size	Male up to 2.5m (8ft) tall; weight up to 130kg (285lb); female smaller
Distribution	Belt of Africa south of Sahara; also south-western Africa
Habitat	Arid regions, deserts, savannah and dry woodland
Diet	Plant material and small animals, including insects
Breeding	Nest a hollow in the ground; male mates with several females, who lay
	1.5kg (3lb 5oz) eggs in one nest; incubation 39–42 days, mainly by male

Greater rhea

Sometimes called the American ostrich, the rhea looks much like a slightly smaller version of the African ostrich. One specific difference is that each foot has three toes, unlike the two toes of the ostrich. Like other ratites (*see opposite*), rheas cannot fly, but they may raise their wings to gain some lift when running fast. Their social behaviour is also similar to that of ostriches. They live in flocks of up to 30 or even more birds. These break up in the breeding season when rival males compete to attract several females, which all lay their eggs in the same nest. The male then incubates them and cares for the young. The smaller Darwin's (or lesser) rhea (*Pterocnemia pennata*) lives in the Andes.

Scientific name	*Rhea americana*
Family	Rheidae
Size	Up to 1.3m (4ft 3in) tall; weight up to 25kg (55lb)
Distribution	South America east of Andes, from Amazon basin to Argentina
Habitat	Open plains, especially with long grass
Diet	Plant roots, leaves and seeds, and small animals including insects
Breeding	Nest a grass-lined depression made by male; each of several females lays up to ten eggs, incubated by male for 35–40 days

Southern or Australian cassowary

The flightless cassowary is recognizibly related to the ostrich and rhea, but it has a distinctive bony casque or helmet on its head, a bright blue head and neck, and red neck wattles. Its legs are shorter and sturdier than those of the ostrich, but equally powerful; the three toes are armed with sharp claws that it uses as weapons in fights. The glossy black feathers are rather like coarse hairs. Cassowaries live alone for most of the year but form pairs in June to October, the dry season. After mating and laying her eggs, the female leaves the male to incubate them and raise the young. She may mate with up to three males, laying separate clutches of eggs.

Scientific name	*Casuarius casuarius*
Family	Casuariidae
Size	Up to 1.5–1.8m (5–6ft) tall; female slightly bigger than male
Distribution	North-eastern Australia; southern New Guinea and nearby islands
Habitat	Rainforest
Diet	Mainly fallen fruits and seeds; sometimes insects and small animals
Breeding	Nest a depression on forest floor; 3–5 green eggs, 140mm (5½in) long, incubated by male for about 60 days. Female polyandrous

Emu

A fast runner that cannot fly, the emu is the obvious Australian counterpart to the ostrich, and is second in size and weight only to the ostrich among all living birds. It can run at 50km/h (30mph), sometimes more, and lives in nomadic groups in open country. These groups may travel long distances for food. The females are slightly larger than the males and have more strongly blue-coloured bare skin on the head and neck. Both sexes have shaggy brown feathers. Males and females pair off in autumn (April or May), but after egg-laying the females rejoin the group while the males incubate the eggs and raise the chicks. Farmers have killed many emus.

Scientific name	*Dromaius novaehollandiae*
Family	Dromaiidae
Size	Up to 2m (6ft 6in) tall; weight up to 50kg (110lb); male slightly smaller
Distribution	Most of mainland Australia except east coast and central Victoria
Habitat	Open plains and dry tropical forest
Diet	Seeds, fruits, leaves, insects and other small creatures
Breeding	Nest a slight hollow in ground lined with trampled vegetation; usually 7–12 dark green eggs, up to 900g (2lb), incubated 55–60 days by male

Brown kiwi

New Zealand's national bird is quite unlike the other ratites and is sometimes put in a group of its own. It is probably related to the giant – up to 3m (10ft) tall – moa, which was hunted to extinction more than 300 years ago. Three kiwi species live in New Zealand, the brown or common kiwi being the biggest. It is a nocturnal, burrowing forest-dweller with poor eyesight but – rare for a bird – has a good sense of smell. It is a squat, pear-shaped bird with no tail, vestigial wings hidden among the feathers, robust legs, and a long bill with nostrils at the tip. There are three subspecies; they vary slightly in colour but all are reddish- or greyish-brown.

Scientific name	*Apteryx australis*
Family	Apterygidae
Size	50–60cm (20–24in) long; female larger than male
Distribution	New Zealand (North Island, South Island and Stewart Island)
Habitat	Forest, and some scrub and grasslands
Diet	Earthworms and other small forest invertebrates, seeds and berries
Breeding	Breeds all year. Nest a burrow; one or two eggs – largest of all birds' in relation to body size – incubated by female, then male, for 71–84 days

Elegant or crested tinamou

Tinamous are ground-living birds that look more like game birds, such as grouse and partridges, than the rheas and other ratites that are their closest relatives. They live in South America. Unlike the ratites, their breastbone is keeled for the attachment of flight muscles, but they are only poor fliers. The elegant tinamou, or martineta, is well adapted for living on the open pampas – camouflaged by the striped 'cryptic' colouring of its plumage – and is a fast runner. Like most ratites, it has three front toes, but also one at the back of each foot. It is easily identified by the slender curving crest on the head of both sexes. It lives part of the year in flocks.

Scientific name	*Eudromia elegans*
Family	Tinamiformes
Size	40cm (16in) long; female slightly larger than male
Distribution	Most of Argentina; parts of eastern Chile
Habitat	Grassland and scrub
Diet	Seeds, fruits and insects
Breeding	Nest a hollow in the ground made by male; six or seven glossy eggs, incubated for about 18–20 days by male

Emperor penguin

The largest of all the penguins, the emperor penguin is confined to the icy shores of Antarctica and never makes a nest. What is more, it breeds during the extreme cold of the Antarctic winter at temperatures as low as –40°C (–40°F). The male incubates the egg by placing it on his feet and covering it with a fold of abdominal skin. Large groups of such males huddle together for warmth, eating nothing for about three months and losing one-third or more of their body weight. Once the chick has hatched, the female returns to care for it while the male heads out to sea to feed. The timing of this breeding cycle means that the young penguin has the best chance of fending for itself in the Antarctic summer.

Scientific name	*Aptenodytes forsteri*
Family	Spheniscidae
Size	Up to 1.2m (4ft) tall; weight 35–45kg (75–100lb) at heaviest
Distribution	Coasts and offshore region of Antarctica
Habitat	Ice and cold seawater
Diet	Fish and squid, sometimes diving as deep as 400m (1300ft)
Breeding	No nest, but pairs occupy same patch of shore each year; single egg laid in May, incubated by male (*see above*) for 62–64 days

Gentoo penguin

A white headband, widening into triangles behind the eyes, makes the gentoo penguin easy to recognize. The yellow bill becomes a more prominent orange-red during the breeding season. At that time, both males and females parade with their bills pointed upwards and make loud trumpeting calls as part of their courtship display. Like other penguins, gentoos are social birds living in colonies – but these are generally smaller than most other penguin colonies, often as few as 50 birds. Although they are found on the Antarctic coast, gentoos also breed as far north as the Falklands and Macquarie Island. Such birds stay near their 'home' island all year, but Antarctic gentoos move north in winter.

Scientific name	*Pygoscelis papua*
Family	Spheniscidae
Size	76cm (30in) tall
Distribution	Antarctic coasts and offshore islands as far north as Falkland Islands
Habitat	Antarctic and subantarctic seas; ice, beaches and tundra
Diet	Fish, squid and crustaceans
Breeding	Breeds in spring. Large cup-shaped nest of vegetation where available; two or sometimes three eggs incubated by both sexes for 35–36 days

Adélie penguin

The Adélie penguin is the most numerous of Antarctic penguins, nesting in vast colonies – hundreds of thousands of birds in some cases – on rocky or stony slopes and flats. They spend the whole winter at sea, and in spring may have to cross up to 100km (60 miles) of pack-ice to reach these breeding grounds. But once the young are born the ice has broken up and open sea is nearby. Like all penguins, Adélies are much more at home in the water than on land, using their flippers – reduced wings – to 'fly' underwater. On ice, they often 'toboggan' on their belly, and then fling themselves in a shallow dive into the sea. To return to land, they leap directly onto an ice-floe that may be several times their own height.

Scientific name	*Pygoscelis adeliae*
Family	Spheniscidae
Size	71cm (28in) tall
Distribution	Offshore waters and coastline of Antarctica
Habitat	Cold seawater; pack-ice and rocky or stony shores
Diet	Crustaceans (mainly krill); small fish
Breeding	Nest a low mound of pebbles or rock-chips made by male; usually two eggs, incubated for 35–36 days by both sexes

Chinstrap penguin

Chinstraps are closely related to Adélie penguins, but are easily distinguished by the white cheeks around the bill, edged underneath by a thin black 'chinstrap'. They are found in much the same areas as Adélies, but also venture farther north onto subantarctic islands. Where the two species share territories, the chinstraps tend to nest on the steeper, more broken ground. They are aggressive to intruders, hissing, growling and stamping their feet as they advance on the interloper. Both species perform a dramatic display when pairs form or re-form in the breeding season. The male extends his head and bill upwards, waving from side to side and uttering a characteristic call. The female may match him.

Scientific name	*Pygoscelis antarctica*
Family	Spheniscidae
Size	68cm (27in) tall
Distribution	Antarctic seas, coasts and nearby islands, as far N as South Georgia
Habitat	Cold seawater; pack-ice and rocky or stony shores
Diet	Crustaceans (mainly krill); small fish
Breeding	Nest a low mound of pebbles or rock-chips made by male; usually two greenish-white eggs, incubated for 35–38 days by both sexes

23

Rockhopper penguin

Unless 'tobogganing', most penguins move about on land with an ungainly – and, to human eyes, amusing – waddling gait. This is because their legs are so short and are positioned so far back on their torpedo-shaped bodies. The rockhopper has another way: as its name suggests, it hops or jumps with both feet together, like a person doing a sack race. It is one of several species with a yellow stripe above each eye extending into tufted yellow crest feathers. It is the most common of the crested penguins and in some places lives in huge colonies of as many as 2½ million birds. They have a strict hierarchy dominated by the biggest breeding males and enforced by cries and displays.

Scientific name	*Eudyptes chrysocome* or *Eudyptes cristatus*
Family	Spheniscidae
Size	61cm (24in) tall
Distribution	Subantarctic islands and seas N to Cape Horn, Australia, New Zealand
Habitat	Cold seas; rocky coasts, beaches, screes and tussocked slopes
Diet	Mainly small crustaceans and squid
Breeding	Nest a shallow hollow edged with stones or plants; two eggs, incubated by both sexes for 33–34 days (but usually only one survives)

Jackass penguin

Jackass penguins belong to a group of penguin species that all have prominent white stripes on the otherwise black sides of the head and body. They live near the western and southern coasts of Namibia and South Africa, where an upwelling of nutrient-rich cold ocean currents results in rich anchovy and pilchard fisheries. As a result, the penguins compete for food with the fishing industry, and overfishing has resulted in a sharp cut in penguin numbers in recent years. Jackass penguins nest in burrows, but because they live in dense colonies, they perform elaborate displays and make complex calls to defend their territories and recognize mates.

Scientific name	*Spheniscus demersus*
Family	Spheniscidae
Size	66cm (26in) tall
Distribution	Seas and coasts of south-western and southern Africa
Habitat	Coastal waters and offshore islands
Diet	Small fish
Breeding	Nest a burrow in sand dunes or niche between rocks; two eggs, incubated by both sexes for about 39 days

Galápagos penguin

Together with the closely related Humboldt or Peruvian penguin (*Spheniscus humboldti*) of the west coast of South America, the Galápagos penguin is the only species to inhabit the tropics. It is, in fact, the most northerly of all penguins, living virtually on the Equator. But this is at the northern end of the cold Humboldt Current, which sweeps up the South American coast and is rich in small fish such as anchovies and pilchards. These provide plentiful food for both the Galápagos and Humboldt species – except in years when an erratic patch of warm sea known as *El Niño* halts the nutrient-rich current. Then the fish disappear and the penguins – like the local fishing industry – suffer severely.

Scientific name	*Spheniscus mendiculus*
Family	Spheniscidae
Size	51cm (20in) tall
Distribution	Galápagos Islands
Habitat	Islands and coastal waters
Diet	Small surface-shoaling fish
Breeding	Breeds at any time of year. Nest made of stones in a cave or rock crevice on the coast; two eggs, incubated by both sexes

Common loon, or great northern diver

This bird is known as the common loon in North America and the great northern diver in Britain. It is easier to hear its eerie wailing, yodelling call than to see the bird, as it is very shy. It spends the breeding season on cold northern lakes in North America, Greenland and Iceland, when its plumage shows a bold black and white pattern. It is a much duller grey-brown in winter, when it migrates to coastal waters of western Europe and North America as far south as Florida and Baja California. It walks poorly, but is an excellent swimmer. It can dive as deep as 60m (200ft) and swim long distances underwater; it may remain submerged for several minutes.

Scientific name	*Gavia immer*
Family	Gaviidae
Size	Male up to 82cm (32in) long; female slightly smaller
Distribution	Northern Hemisphere from Scandinavia to Alaska; migrates S in winter
Habitat	Cold northern lakes in summer; coastal waters in winter
Diet	Small fish; shellfish; crustaceans; aquatic insects; frogs
Breeding	Nest a low pile of plant materials at edge of lake or on an island; usually two dark olive-brown eggs, incubated by both sexes for 25–29 days

Little grebe, or dabchick

Grebes have similarities to divers or loons, but recent research shows that they are not so closely related as once believed. They are very widespread, and the little grebe, or dabchick – one of the smallest species – is found in large areas of the Eastern Hemisphere. In summer, the neck and sides of the head have a rusty-red patch, but these parts are a buff colour in winter. It looks quite dumpy, but like all grebes is well adapted for diving and plunges frequently to a depth of a metre (yard) or more in the small lakes and ponds it inhabits. It can stay submerged for 10 to 20 seconds, searching for small aquatic creatures to eat.

Scientific name	*Podiceps* (or *Tachybaptus*) *ruficolis*
Family	Podicipedidae
Size	25–29cm (10–11in) long
Distribution	Much of Europe, Asia and Africa; migrates from cold regions in winter
Habitat	Small, well-vegetated lakes, ponds and slow rivers; estuaries in winter
Diet	Aquatic insects and molluscs; shrimps; tadpoles; small fish
Breeding	Nest a semi-floating mass of vegetation at edge of lake made by both sexes; four to six eggs, incubated by both sexes for 20–21 days

Slavonian or horned grebe

Closely related to the well-known great crested grebe (*Podiceps cristatus*) of Europe and Asia, the more widespread Salvonian grebe (known in North America as the horned grebe) has a less pronounced crest on its head. But its summer plumage is more colourful – a rich red-brown on the neck and underparts, and a black head with golden ear-tufts (the 'horns') stretching up and back from each eye. Both species perform an elaborate courtship 'dance' in the water before mating, with both male and female rising up, breast-to-breast, in the water. The presence of grebes is a good indication of clean, unpolluted water with many fish.

Scientific name	*Podiceps auritus*
Family	Podicipedidae
Size	31–36cm (12–14in) long
Distribution	Breeds across central Europe, Asia and North America; winters farther S
Habitat	Clean lakes and ponds; winters on lakes, estuaries and sheltered coasts
Diet	Fish; aquatic insects and crustaceans
Breeding	Nest a semi-floating platform of weeds among vegetation at edge of lake; three to five eggs incubated by both sexes for 22–25 days

Wandering albatross

No bird is more aptly named, for none is better adapted for gliding flight. It breeds in colonies on isolated oceanic islands, but its real realm is the ocean itself. It is the biggest of all ocean birds and can travel vast distances without beating its wings – the longest of any bird's – simply by riding on air currents. Satellite tracking studies have shown that a bird may travel up to 15 000km (9300 miles), at speeds of up to 80km/h (50mph), in a ten-day period. The wandering albatross rarely alights on the water, except at night to feed. It does this mainly by dipping its head into the water to catch creatures that rise to the surface at night; rarely, it makes shallow dives. Wandering albatrosses live 30 years or more.

Scientific name	*Diomedea exulans*
Family	Diomedeidae
Size	Up to 1.4m (4ft 6in) long; wingspan up to 3.4m (11ft)
Distribution	Southern Atlantic, Indian and Pacific Oceans mostly S of 25–30°S
Habitat	Open ocean and isolated oceanic islands; coasts of southern continents
Diet	Cuttlefish, squid and fish; scrounges from ships
Breeding	Pairs for life, breeding every two years. Nest a hollowed mound of earth and vegetation; single egg incubated by both sexes for 70–82 days

Black-footed albatross

This is one of only three species of albatross that breed in the Northern Hemisphere – including, in the case of the black-footed albatross, on the Hawaiian Islands. It is one of a group of smaller albatrosses known as 'mollymawks' – from the Dutch *mollemok* (foolish gull), a name originally applied to the fulmar (*see p.34*). Its plumage is almost entirely grey-black to brown, except for white markings at the base of the tail and bill. In common with other members of the order Procellariiformes, it has tubular nostrils (which in albatrosses lie on either side of the upper bill) and well-developed olfactory (smell) lobes of the brain; they probably locate food, breeding sites and mate by smell.

Scientific name	*Diomedea nigripes*
Family	Diomedeidae
Size	About 72cm (28in) long; wingspan about 2m (6ft 6in)
Distribution	North Pacific, usually N of about 20°N
Habitat	Open ocean and oceanic islands
Diet	Cuttlefish, squid and fish; scrounges from ships
Breeding	Breeds in winter, in colonies on sandy beaches and atolls. Nest a shallow hollow; single egg incubated by both sexes for about 70 days

Fulmar

Sometimes called the northern fulmar to distinguish it from the southern or Antarctic species (*Fulmarus glacialoides*), the fulmar has increased enormously in numbers since the beginning of the 20th century. One reason is the growth of fish-processing by factory ships; fulmars are accomplished scroungers of the waste from these ships. In colouring they resemble gulls, but the birds are not related. Fulmars are heavily built, with a stout bill, but they are strong fliers that alternate a few strong beats of their stiff wings with long glides. Unlike albatrosses – but like the other members of the group – their tubular nostrils are on the top of the bill.

Scientific name	*Fulmarus glacialis*
Family	Procellariidae
Size	Up to 47cm (18½in) long; wingspan up to 1.12m (3ft 8in)
Distribution	Arctic, Atlantic and Pacific Oceans and coasts mostly N of 40–45°N
Habitat	Open ocean and coasts (especially where rocky); winters at sea
Diet	Fish and drifting marine organisms; scrounges from ships
Breeding	Breeds on cliffs, laying single egg on bare rock crevice or in hollow in vegetation; incubated by both sexes for 52–53 days

Cape or pintado petrel

Early whalers in the Southern Ocean thought that this bird – which wheeled around their boats scrounging food – resembled a pigeon. So they called it the Cape pigeon. Despite the chequered plumage, it is of course totally unrelated to pigeons, and its flight pattern – alternating rapid wingbeats and stiff-winged glides – is a clue to its relationship to fulmars, other petrels and shearwaters. Unlike shearwaters (which feed on the wing), Cape petrels alight on the water to feed, dipping their head or diving shallowly to catch sea creatures. Like a number of southern petrels, it ranges as far north as the Equator off the Pacific coast of South America, where the cold Humboldt Current supplies food.

Scientific name	*Daption capense*
Family	Procellariidae
Size	Up to 39cm (15½in) long; wingspan about 1m (3ft 3in)
Distribution	Southern Atlantic, Indian and Pacific Oceans and coasts mostly S of 25°S
Habitat	Open ocean, islands and coasts of southern continents; winters at sea
Diet	Fish, squid and other marine organisms
Breeding	Breeds in small colonies on coasts and islands. Nest a hollow in rock fragments on ledge or in crevice; single egg incubated by both sexes

Great shearwater

Shearwaters are named for their habit of gliding low over the sea, skimming the wave-tops and dipping for food. Like many other members of the group, they are great travellers. The great shearwater breeds in the southern summer on Tristan da Cunha and Gough Island, 40°S in the South Atlantic. As winter nears, the birds head north for the northern summer, where they first feed off New England and eastern Canada. Then they cross the North Atlantic towards Iceland and the coasts of western Europe before heading south again in October. Closely related Pacific species make similar epic travels around that ocean. Some species, known as muttonbirds, have long been caught for meat.

Scientific name	*Puffinus gravis* (Note: Not related to puffin)
Family	Procellariidae
Size	Up to 50cm (19½in) long; wingspan about 1.15m (3ft 9in)
Distribution	North and South Atlantic Oceans and coasts (migrates)
Habitat	Open ocean, oceanic islands and coasts
Diet	Fish, squid and other marine organisms
Breeding	Breeds in colonies on isolated South Atlantic islands. Single egg incubated by both sexes for about 55 days

Wilson's storm-petrel

The group that includes the biggest ocean birds – the great albatrosses – also contains the smallest, for most storm-petrels are little bigger than sparrows. Yet they are true ocean travellers, hardly touching land except to breed. Wilson's storm-petrel is one of the species native to the Southern Hemisphere (although it migrates as far north as Greenland in the southern winter). These birds have longer legs than the Northern Hemisphere storm-petrels, and they hold them dangling down as the bird flutters close to the water, bouncing and 'walking' on the surface of the sea. They use their feet to pick up small fish and other creatures.

Scientific name	*Oceanites oceanicus*
Family	Hydrobatidae, or sometimes included in Procellariidae
Size	17–18cm (about 7in) long; wingspan about 40cm (16in)
Distribution	Southern oceans, islands and coasts; winters at sea, as far N as 60°N
Habitat	Open ocean; sometimes oceanic islands and coasts
Diet	Small fish, crustaceans and other sea creatures
Breeding	Breeds on coasts of Antarctica and nearby islands. Nests in burrows in slope facing sea; single egg incubated by both sexes for about 55 days

Red-tailed tropicbird

Few seabirds are as elegant as the tropicbirds, especially red-tailed tropicbirds. Their white body plumage develops a beautiful pink tinge when breeding (which occurs at various seasons, depending on location). This is the only time that they are commonly seen near land; they are true oceanic birds that wander alone, plunge-diving into the sea for their food. They are far less mobile on land, waddling on their short legs and small webbed feet, and have to nest on a site where they can launch themselves into the air for flight. Even their courtship display takes place in the air. The tail feathers have been long prized for adornment by Pacific islanders.

Scientific name	*Phaethon rubricauda*
Family	Phaethonidae
Size	92cm (3ft) long, including tail; wingspan up to 1m (3ft 3in)
Distribution	Tropical and subtropical Indian and Pacific Oceans and islands
Habitat	Open ocean; oceanic islands and coasts when breeding
Diet	Fish, squid and other marine creatures
Breeding	Nests in colonies, mainly on cliffs and ledges. Single egg laid on bare ground, or in crevice or hole; incubated by both sexes for 40–45 days

Australian pelican

Pelican species live on or near water in the warmer parts of all the continents except Antarctica. Although their pouched bill – used for scooping up fish, usually by reaching under water – makes them look comical, a flock of pelicans swimming or flying in stately formation is a fascinating and beautiful sight. It is only on land, or when scampering on the water to take off, that they look ungainly – with good reason, for pelicans are among the bulkiest and heaviest of flying birds. Some species prefer salt water, some prefer fresh; the Australian pelican is indifferent, living on fresh- and salt-water lakes, lagoons, swamps, rivers and estuaries.

Scientific name	*Pelecanus conspicillatus*
Family	Pelecanidae
Size	Up to 1.7m (5ft 6in) long, including bill; weight up to 15kg (33lb)
Distribution	Australia and southern New Guinea
Habitat	On or near any large area of fresh, brackish or salt water
Diet	Fish and crustaceans
Breeding	Breeds any time of year, in colonies. Nest a platform of sticks and plants on ground; two to four eggs, incubated by both sexes for 32–35 days

Common or northern gannet

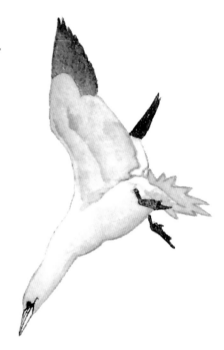

Gannets are spectacular plunge-divers. They fold their wings back and plummet from a height of 30m (100ft) or more into the sea to catch their food. Powerful goose-sized birds (the name *gannet* comes from the same root as *gander*), they are powerful fliers that venture far out to sea. Gannets have a strong migratory instinct, those breeding on the coasts of north-western Europe wintering in the Canary Islands and West Africa, those from Greenland and north-eastern North America flying to the Gulf of Mexico. They nest in huge colonies of many thousands of birds on isolated rocks such as Bass Rock and St Kilda in Scotland and Bird Rock, Canada.

Scientific name	*Morus bassanus* or *Sula bassana*
Family	Sulidae
Size	84–95cm (33–37in) long; wingspan up to 1.7m (5ft 6in)
Distribution	North Atlantic (arc from eastern USA to British Isles); migrate S in winter
Habitat	Coasts and mainly relatively shallow seas
Diet	Shoaling fish such as herring and mackerel
Breeding	Nest of mud and seaweed made by both sexes on cliff ledge or flat ground; single egg incubated by both sexes for about 44 days

Brown booby

Boobies are so called because of their fearless – to early observers, 'stupid' – behaviour and appearance. They seem to have no fear of people, and owe their survival to the fact that they breed on little-visited isolated islands. Boobies are also known for their colourful feet, which are red, blue or greenish in various species; those of the brown booby – probably the commonest of the species in the tropics – are greenish-yellow. Brown boobies resemble rather lightly built gannets, and are in fact closely related. Like gannets, they dive-bomb for fish and can then stay submerged for up to 40 seconds, swimming with feet and wings after their prey.

Scientific name	*Sula leucogaster*
Family	Sulidae
Size	Up to 74cm (29in) long; wingspan up to 1.5m (5ft)
Distribution	Tropical and subtropical parts of all the oceans
Habitat	Oceans, especially near islands where they breed
Diet	Fish (especially flying fish) and squid
Breeding	Breeds at any time of year. Nest of sticks built as part of courting ritual;
	usually two eggs, incubated for about 50 days; stronger chick kills other

Great or common cormorant

Cormorants are clumsy on land but accomplished underwater swimmers, propelled by big feet in which all four toes (as in all members of this group) are joined by webbing. In eastern Asia, captive great cormorants and the slightly smaller Japanese species (*Phalacrocorax capillatus*) have for centuries been used to catch fish while tethered to a line. The bird has a ring around its neck to prevent it swallowing the fish it catches. (Cormorants in any case normally swallow their catch only after they come to the surface.) It is later freed of the ring to feed itself. All cormorants swim characteristically low on the surface of the water, with much of the body submerged, watching for fish to dive and chase.

Scientific name	*Phalacrocorax carbo*
Family	Phalacrocoracidae
Size	86–91cm (34–36in) long
Distribution	Most of Europe and Asia; parts of North America, Africa and Australia
Habitat	Coasts; islands; large inland waterways
Diet	Bottom-feeding and midwater fish up to about 20cm (8in) long
Breeding	May breed twice in year. Nest of seaweed and/or twigs on flat rock or in waterside tree; usually three or four eggs, incubated for 23–30 days

Double-crested cormorant

This species, the most common North American cormorant, is slightly smaller than the great cormorant but similar in overall colouring. The curly black and white head crests, for which it is named, are seen only during the breeding season. At other times, its most distinctive feature is the bright orange throat. Despite being a good underwater swimmer, its plumage – like that of all cormorants – is not well waterproofed with oil. For this reason, cormorants often extend their wings to dry when they are resting out of the water. Despite their rather short wings, they are strong fliers, propelling themselves with steady wingbeats.

Scientific name	*Phalacrocorax auritus*
Family	Phalacrocoracidae
Size	About 80cm (31in) long
Distribution	North America from Alaska and Newfoundland to Mexico and Cuba
Habitat	Coasts; islands; large rivers; lakes
Diet	Fish
Breeding	Nest usually of twigs, in waterside tree; two to four eggs, incubated by both sexes for 25–29 days

43

Anhinga or water-turkey

The anhinga – also called the darter or, in North America, the water-turkey – looks rather like a long-necked, sharp-billed cormorant, and the birds are indeed closely related. When stalking underwater prey, the anhinga keeps its neck bent in an S shape; when within range, its head darts forward to spear the fish it has been hunting on its sharp bill; this action is the origin of the name darter. On the surface, it tosses the fish into the air, catches and manoeuvres it head-down, then swallows it whole. Anhingas often swim along on the surface with only their head and curved neck showing – hence yet another common name, snake bird.

Scientific name	*Anhinga anhinga*
Family	Anhingidae
Size	About 90cm (35in) long
Distribution	South-eastern USA to Argentina
Habitat	Freshwater lakes, rivers and swamps; rarely, brackish water
Diet	Fish; crayfish; frogs; aquatic insects
Breeding	Nests in small colonies. Nest of twigs built in waterside bush or tree; three to six bluish-white eggs incubated by both sexes for 25–28 days

Lesser frigate bird

Frigate birds are the greatest fliers of the pelican group, their vast wings enabling them to soar effortlessly in the tropical skies. Yet they have the webbed feet of their allies. They often feed at the water surface, but prefer more piratical ways of getting their food, and are sometimes known as pirate birds or man-o'-war birds. Their usual method is to chase and harass a booby, gull or other seabird until it disgorges or drops its own catch in order to make a quicker escape. The attacker then swoops to catch the falling food in mid-air. The males of all five frigate bird species have a red throat patch which they inflate when attracting a female.

Scientific name	*Fregata ariel*
Family	Fregatidae
Size	About 75cm (30in) long; wingspan 1.75m (5ft 8in)
Distribution	Tropical and subtropical Indian and Pacific Oceans; also off Brazil
Habitat	Oceans; oceanic islands and coasts
Diet	Fish (especially flying fish); other surface-living marine creatures
Breeding	Nest built by female in tree or on bare ground using twigs collected or stolen by male; single egg incubated by both sexes for about 45 days

Great white egret

This beautiful, majestic bird is found in parts of every continent except Antarctica. It is sometimes called the American egret or great white heron. It is similar in colouring to the little egret (*Egretta garzetta*), which is more widespread than the great egret in Europe, but it stands almost twice as tall. Like many other members of the family, it is often seen standing motionless or walking slowly in shallow water, stalking its prey; it then pounces with a rapid thrust of its sharp, narrow bill. The bill is normally yellow, but turns almost black as the breeding season approaches. The great egret flies, neck drawn back, with slow, deliberate beats of its huge wings – which span up to 1.7m (5ft 6in).

Scientific name	*Egretta alba, Ardea alba* or *Casmerodius alba*
Family	Ardeidae
Size	About 86–102cm (34–40in) long; American subspecies slightly larger
Distribution	Almost worldwide in warm regions; in Europe, mainly in south-east
Habitat	Marshes, swamps, river-banks, shallow lakes and lagoons
Diet	Fish and other small aquatic creatures
Breeding	Nests in small groups, usually in reed-beds or in trees or bushes; two to five eggs, incubated by both sexes for 23–26 days

Western reef heron

Most herons are found on or near shallow inland waters, but reef herons are primarily coastal birds. There are two rather similar species, inhabiting coasts from the Red Sea to eastern Asia and Australasia. The western species rarely strays as far north and west as the Mediterranean. Both species of reef heron have two colour phases, or forms: a dark, slate-gray form (illustrated here) that is normally seen at higher, temperate latitudes, and a white form that is more common in the tropics. However, the two forms interbreed, and a single brood may contain both dark and light-coloured birds. Reef herons look rather less elegant than other egrets, with shorter plumes and a thicker, slightly curved bill.

Scientific name	*Egretta gulgaris*; eastern species: *Egretta sacra*
Family	Ardeidae
Size	55–70cm (21½–27½in) long
Distribution	Red Sea and western Indian Ocean coasts
Habitat	Coral reefs; rock platforms; beaches
Diet	Fish; prawns and other marine invertebrates
Breeding	Nest a rough platform of sticks in a rock crevice, cave or other hidden place; usually two or three eggs, incubated by both sexes for 25–28 days

White-crested tiger heron

Tiger herons are intermediate in many characteristics between other herons and the shorter, stockier bitterns, and this species is sometimes called the white-crested bittern. Like bitterns, tiger herons tend to be solitary, make booming mating calls, and have cryptic (patterned) colouring that helps concealment. (Their name comes from these supposedly tiger-like markings.) However, like other herons, they have three or four tufts of powder-down feathers – special feathers that crumble to form a powder that the birds use to dress their other feathers and remove oil and grease – on each side of the body. True bitterns have only two pairs of such patches. Tiger herons hunt for food mainly at night.

Scientific name	*Tigriornis leucolophus*
Family	Ardeidae
Size	66–80cm (26–31½in) long
Distribution	Central and west Africa
Habitat	Tropical swamps and forests near rivers
Diet	Believed to be river fish and other aquatic creatures
Breeding	Believed to nest in trees near rivers; other details of breeding habits unknown

American bittern

Bitterns are shy birds that, if disturbed, stand perfectly still with their head and bill held vertically. This attitude and their colouring make them merge into their background of reeds so well that they are almost impossible to spot. In fact, they are far more likely to be heard than seen, for the males' mating call carries long distances. It is often described as a booming, gulping or belching sound, and from close-by a heavy intake of breath can be heard before each boom. The sound has given the bird such local nicknames as 'thunder-pumper' and 'stake-driver'. The Eurasian bittern (*Botaurus stellaris*) is slightly bigger than the American species, and has more pronounced markings on its back.

Scientific name	*Botaurus lentiginosus*
Family	Ardeidae
Size	60–76cm (24–30in) long
Distribution	Temperate North America, migrating S in winter
Habitat	Reedbeds; sometimes wet meadows
Diet	Fish, frogs and other small aquatic creatures
Breeding	Nest of reeds built by female in reedbed or alongside river or lake; three to six brownish eggs, incubated by both sexes for 25–28 days

Yellow-crowned night heron

Night herons are, as their name suggests, most active at night, when they mainly feed. However, they are not entirely nocturnal, and are often seen also by day flying from one treetop roost to another. They are stocky birds with a rather short neck and a thick bill. The yellow-crowned species is mostly slate-grey with white cheeks and a yellowish or whitish crown and head plumes. It usually keeps its neck tucked in, both in flight and often also at rest. It has longer legs than the closely related black-crowned night heron (*Nicticorax nycticorax*), which is probably the most numerous of all herons, found on every warm continent. Its yellow-crowned relative is restricted to the Americas.

Scientific name	*Nyctanassa violacea*
Family	Ardeidae
Size	56–70cm (22–28in) long
Distribution	North and South America, from United States to Brazil and Peru
Habitat	Swamps; thick woodland near coasts
Diet	Mostly aquatic invertebrates such as crayfish and crabs; some fish
Breeding	Nest of twigs, usually in tree or bush; usually three to five pale bluish-green eggs, incubated by both sexes for 21–25 days

Boat-billed heron

The boat-billed heron's bill is so different from that of any other members of the group that at one time the bird was classified in a separate family. The bill is slipper-like, about 8cm (3in) long and 5cm (2in) wide, and deeply curved on the underside. The boat-billed heron feeds at night – aided in dim light by its big eyes – and its bill is highly sensitive. The bird is believed to dabble in the water with its bill for food even in total darkness; at the slightest touch of its small aquatic prey the bill opens, drawing in water and prey. In other respects, the boat-billed heron is much like other night-hunting herons, with a stocky body and short legs. It has a drooping, fan-shaped crest of black feathers on its head.

Scientific name	*Cochlearius cochlearius*
Family	Ardeidae
Size	45–51cm (18–20in) long
Distribution	Central and South America, from Mexico to northern Argentina
Habitat	Mangrove swamps and other freshwater and brackish wetlands
Diet	Small fish, shrimps and other aquatic creatures
Breeding	Nest a platform of twigs in mangroves or other swamp trees, alone or in small groups; two to four eggs, incubated by both sexes

Marabou stork

One of the largest flying birds, the marabou is a striking but not – to our eyes – very elegant or attractive bird. It has long, rather ungainly legs, a massive wedge-shaped bill and a bare neck with a large hanging wattle, or pouch, which it inflates with air during mating displays. Its scavenging habits – it competes with vultures for the first pick of the flesh of rotting animal carcasses – also seem unappealing, but marabous do an important job in helping to recycle dead organic matter. (Once opened up by a marabou, a carcass can be attacked by other, weaker scavengers.) On the wing, however, marabou storks look majestic as they soar or fly with slow beats of their great wings – which span up to 2.6m (8ft 6in).

Scientific name	*Leptoptilos crumeniferus*
Family	Ciconiidae
Size	About 1.5m (5ft) long
Distribution	Most of Africa south of Sahara
Habitat	Open grasslands and marshes, often near human settlements
Diet	Animal carcasses; small live mammals, birds, eggs, insects and fish
Breeding	Nests in colonies in trees or on cliffs. Nest of sticks with central hollow; three to five eggs, incubated by both sexes for about 30 days

Shoebill, or whale-headed stork

This extraordinary-looking bird has many both stork-like and heron-like anatomical and behavioural characteristics. But its most obvious feature – the massive hooked bill – is unique; it is 20cm (8in) long and almost as wide, and is shaped like a clog, or wooden shoe. The shoebill is usually placed in a family of its own within the group that includes herons and storks, but DNA evidence has recently suggested that it may be more closely related to another group of big-billed birds, the pelicans. It is a shy bird of dense swamps, where it stands motionless for long periods or wades slowly through the shallows searching for prey – on which it then lunges with its whole body.

Scientific name	*Balaeniceps rex*
Family	Balaenicipitidae; according to some scientists, Pelecanidae
Size	About 1.2m (4ft) long
Distribution	Eastern central Africa (Sudan to Congo and Zambia)
Habitat	Freshwater swamps (especially papyrus swamps of the Sudd)
Diet	Fish (especially lungfish), amphibians, reptiles and other aquatic animals
Breeding	Nest a large platform of vegetation at water level; two eggs, incubated (and sometimes cooled with water) by both sexes for about 30 days

Scarlet ibis

Scarlet ibises are highly social birds, breeding and feeding in large flocks. Such a flock is a stunning sight, for no other shore or wading bird has such brilliant red plumage. But the pale colour of many birds kept in zoos shows the importance of diet – in the wild, an ample supply of shrimps – for the scarlet colouring. Unfortunately, the scarlet ibis has long been hunted by people both for its feathers and as food, and numbers declined enormously during the 20th century. It is the national bird of Trinidad, but for several decades none bred there – until conservation measures in a sanctuary encouraged their return. Ibises probe for their food, using their slender curved bill, while wading in shallow water.

Scientific name	*Eudocimus ruber*
Family	Threskiornithidae
Size	56–76cm (22–30in) long
Distribution	South American coast from Venezuela to Brazil; parts of Caribbean
Habitat	Mudflats; shallow bays and lagoons; mangrove swamps; marshes
Diet	Crustaceans (especially shrimps) and other small aquatic creatures; seeds
Breeding	Nests in colonies of several hundred pairs. Nest a treetop platform of sticks; three to five green eggs, incubated by both sexes for 19–23 days

Roseate spoonbill

The beautiful deep pink, scarlet and white plumage of the roseate spoonbill contrasts strangely with the bare grey-green skin of its head. The most notable feature of all spoonbills is, however, the bill – which broadens at the tip to a rounded and flattened spatula shape. This shape develops only as a young bird matures. Spoonbills feed by sweeping their bill from side to side in the muddy bottom of their feeding grounds. As with the scarlet ibis, the beauty of the roseate spoonbill's feathers has made it a prey for hunters, and this – combined with the destruction and pollution of its swampland breeding habitats – has led to a serious decline in the bird's numbers in recent decades.

Scientific name	*Ajaia ajaja* or *Platalea ajaja*
Family	Threskiornithidae
Size	66–80cm (26–31in) long
Distribution	Americas from Gulf Coast of United States to Argentina
Habitat	Mangrove swamps, lagoons, marshes and other wetlands
Diet	Crustaceans, small fish and other bottom-dwelling aquatic creatures
Breeding	Nests in colonies, often with ibises, egrets and other birds. Nest of twigs in treetop; three to five eggs, incubated by both sexes for 22–24 days

Greater flamingo

With their disproportionately long legs and neck, small head, strangely angled bill and distinctive rosy-pink plumage, flamingos are unmistakable and beautiful, if rather gawky, birds. The greater flamingo is the largest of the four or five species. (Some scientists regard the Chilean flamingo as a separate species, *Phoenicopterus chilensis,* while others classify it as a subspecies of the greater flamingo.) It is also the most widely spread. It is, like all flamingos, highly social, feeding and breeding in large flocks. It feeds standing (or sometimes swimming) in shallow salty water, reaching down with its bill upside-down. It draws water through fine comb-like plates inside the bill to trap small food creatures.

Scientific name	*Phoenicopterus ruber*
Family	Phoenicopteridae
Size	About 1.45m (4ft 9in) long; female slightly smaller
Distribution	Scattered parts of Asia, Africa, south-western Europe and Caribbean
Habitat	Shallow salt and soda lakes; coastal waters
Diet	Marine invertebrates such as shrimps, molluscs and brine fleas
Breeding	May not breed every year. Nest a hollowed mound of mud in shallow water or mudflat; single egg, incubated by both sexes for 28–30 days

Lesser flamingo

Despite having a much more restricted range than the greater flamingo, the lesser species is far more numerous. Some flocks on the highly alkaline soda lakes of East Africa, such as Lake Nakuru, number well over a million birds – a breathtaking sight, whether in flight or feeding in the shallows. They feed in a similar manner to the greater flamingo, but their bill (which is more deeply keeled) has even finer filter plates. These plates can trap the smallest food particles: microscopic animals and plants, including single-celled blue-green algae. Such algae occur in vast 'blooms' in soda lakes; they are rich in carotenoids, substances related to vitamin A that give the flamingos their pink colour.

Scientific name	*Phoenicopterus minor*
Family	Phoenicopteridae
Size	About 1m (3ft 3in) long; female smaller
Distribution	Africa, especially Rift Valley of East Africa
Habitat	Salty and alkaline inland lakes
Diet	Microscopic plankton, especially blue-green algae
Breeding	Nest a hollowed mound of mud in shallow water or mudflat; one or sometimes two eggs, incubated by both sexes for 28–30 days

Horned screamer

With their small head, long legs and toes (virtually without webbing), and short curved bill, screamers are quite unlike any other members of the waterfowl group, and are classified in a separate family. They have two distinctive sharp, bony spurs on the front edge of each wing, and the horned screamer has a strange curved spike projecting from its forehead. Screamers are strong fliers and also, despite the unwebbed feet, swim well; but their feet are particularly adapted to walking on floating vegetation in swamps and jungle lakes. As their name suggests, screamers are noisy birds, making loud calls when flying, walking or roosting in jungle trees.

Scientific name	*Anhima cornuta*
Family	Anhimidae
Size	Up to about 91cm (3ft) long
Distribution	South America, from Guyana to Argentina
Habitat	Marshland; wet grassland; forest lagoons
Diet	Plant material such as fleshy grasses and seeds
Breeding	Shallow ground-level nest of reeds and rushes; two to six large eggs, incubated by both sexes for 42–44 days

Magpie or pied goose

This Australian goose shows several features intermediate between the screamers and other members of the waterfowl group – including a long neck and legs, and only half-webbed feet. The bill is hooked, for digging roots from the soil during the dry season. Another unusual feature is the knob on the bird's head, which grows more prominent with age and tends to be bigger in males than females. Both sexes make a honking call, the male's higher-pitched than the female's. Many (but not all) males mate with two females; such breeding trios share one nest and raise the young as one family. Magpie geese moult gradually and have no flightless period.

Scientific name	*Anseranas semipalmata*
Family	Anatidae; sometimes placed in separate family, Anseranatidae
Size	Up to 91cm (3ft) long; female smaller
Distribution	Northern parts of Australia, mostly near coast; southern New Guinea
Habitat	Marshes; rivers and lakes; wet grassland
Diet	Seeds, roots and other plant material
Breeding	Often polygynous. Nest a large platform of rushes; six to nine eggs laid by each female in same nest, incubated by both sexes for 24–25 days

Whistling tree duck

The name whistling duck comes from the loud whistling calls the birds make to each other, particularly in flight – where the calls are augmented by the sound of their wings. They are small but rather long-legged and long-necked ducks that live in various tropical areas of the world. They fly with a distinctive posture – neck extended and head lowered – that makes them look hunch-backed. Whistling ducks, as the alternative name tree ducks suggests, sometimes perch in trees but they are far more at home in marshy surroundings. Indeed, in Australia the whistling tree duck is often called the water whistling duck. Its breeding cycle is closely linked to the annual wet season, when plant food is plentiful.

Scientific name	*Dendrocygna arcuata*
Family	Anatidae; sometimes placed in separate family, Dendrocygnidae
Size	55–61cm (21½–24in) long; female smaller
Distribution	Philippines; New Guinea; New Britain; northern Australia (near coasts)
Habitat	Tropical lagoons, marshes and other wetlands
Diet	Aquatic plants, including grasses, waterlilies and water gentians
Breeding	Nest a grass-lined hollow in ground some way from water, sheltered by a bush; seven or eight eggs, incubated by both sexes for 28–30 days

Black-necked swan

The biggest and most majestic of all waterfowl, all swans have some combination of black and/or white colouring; the legs, feet and bill are the only parts that show other colours. In the case of the South American black-necked swan, the legs and feet are pink and the bill bluish-grey with a bright red caruncle (lobe) at the base in adults. Most swans are much more at home on water than land, but the black-necked species is the most waterbound of all. It is shy of humans, but lives in sociable groups of its own species out of the breeding season. Its normal voice is a high-pitched soft whistle, although it may honk more noisily when flying.

Scientific name	*Cygnus melanocoryphus*
Family	Anatidae
Size	Up to about 1.2m (4ft) long; female slightly smaller
Distribution	South America, from southern Brazil to Patagonia; Falkland Islands
Habitat	Inland waterways (mainly quite large); river estuaries
Diet	Mainly aquatic vegetation; some insects
Breeding	Nest of loose vegetation in reeds or at edge of lake or river; four to eight eggs, incubated by female for about 36 days; male guards nest

White-fronted goose

The name white-fronted goose may mislead, as it refers to the forehead and base of the bill rather than the chest – which, like most of the rest of its body, is brownish-grey with black bars and blotches on the belly. (The bird is sometimes nicknamed 'specklebelly'.) It is one of a group of five very similar species known as grey geese, and is the only one of these that is seen regularly in North America, from Alaska to central Canada (and much farther south in winter). It also occurs in Greenland and all across northern Europe and Asia. Different geographical populations show variations in bill colouring from pink to orange-red.

Scientific name	Anser albifrons
Family	Anatidae
Size	66–78cm (26–31in) long
Distribution	Northern subarctic (almost circumpolar); migrates S in winter
Habitat	Subarctic tundra and marshes; winters on grassland and fields near sea
Diet	Plant material, including seeds, grain and young shoots; some insects
Breeding	Pairs for life. Nest a hollow in ground lined with grass and down;
	usually five or six eggs, incubated by female for 23–25 days

Hawaiian goose, or néné

By the middle of the 20th century, fewer than 50 Hawaiian geese had survived years of hunting by humans and harassment by feral dogs, cats, rats and other introduced animals. Conservation measures were introduced, and a captive breeding programme was begun in 1949. By 2000 there were almost 1000 Hawaiian geese in the wild on the islands and another 1000 in zoos and other collections around the world. It is still an endangered species, but now has a good chance of survival. The bird – declared Hawaii's state bird in 1957 – is known in the Hawaiian language as the néné (pronounced nay-nay) after the sound it makes when feeding.

Scientific name	*Branta sandvicensis*
Family	Anatidae
Size	58–71cm (23–28in) long; female slightly smaller
Distribution	In wild only in Hawaii
Habitat	Grasslands and other vegetated areas between lava flows on mountains
Diet	Grass and other vegetation, including berries; drinks dew
Breeding	Pairs for life. Breeds in winter (wet season). Nest a hollow in ground lined with down; two to five eggs, incubated by female for 28–30 days

Canada goose

The situation of the Canada goose could hardly be more different from that of its endangered close relative the Hawaiian goose (*see p.63*). It has spread far beyond its original habitat of the North American prairies and subarctic tundra to woods, parks and farmland, and (with human help) as far as the British Isles and New Zealand. In many places it is the largest breeding goose, but among at least 12 known geographical races or subspecies some are no bigger than many ducks. These distinctively marked geese are generally very tame – but are often shot either for sport or because they are so successful that they are regarded as pests.

Scientific name	*Branta canadensis*
Family	Anatidae
Size	Various subspecies 58–115cm (23–45in) long
Distribution	North America; eastern Siberia; introduced to Europe and elsewhere
Habitat	Originally tundra and prairie; has spread to farmland, marshes, parks
Diet	Grasses; other small plants, including aquatic vegetation
Breeding	Nest a grass- and down-lined hollow in ground near water; five or six
	eggs, incubated by female (guarded by male) for 25–30 days

Eurasian pochard

Pochards belong to the group known as diving or bay ducks. They have a heavy body with short legs set well back, and are well built for diving. They prefer open lakes with underwater vegetation, and often dive as deep as 1–2.5m (about 3–8ft) to feed. The common or Eurasian pochard has a very distinctive head shape, but only the male has the rich brown head plumage; as with many ducks, the female is a rather dull grey-brown colour. Closely related species with different colouring include the tufted duck (*Aythya fuligula*) of Asia and Europe, the scaup (*A. marila*) of Asia, Europe and North America, and the American canvasback (*A. valisneria*).

Scientific name	*Aythya ferina*
Family	Anatidae
Size	44–49cm (17–19in) long
Distribution	Much of Europe and Asia as far east as Lake Baikal, except far north
Habitat	Lakes and other (preferably secluded) inland waterways
Diet	Aquatic vegetation (roots; leaves; buds); also small aquatic animals
Breeding	Cup-shaped nest on ground, or on platform in shallow water, protected by reeds; up to 12 eggs, incubated by female for about 28 days

Common or green-winged teal

The distinctive yellow-edged green eye-patch, chestnut-brown head, yellow rump and green wing patch together make the male teal easily recognizable. The female is mostly brown, but also has a green patch on the wing. The teal is one of the smallest and in many areas commonest ducks, but it is a shy bird that prefers well-hidden places, especially for nesting. It is one of the so-called dabbling ducks, which feed on the surface or up-end to nibble plant food in the shallows, but do not dive. Among about 40 close relatives are the blue-winged teal (*Anas discors*), mallard (*A. platyrhynchos*), pintail (*A. acuta*) and shoveller (*A. clypeata*).

Scientific name	*Anas crecca*
Family	Anatidae
Size	34–38cm (13–15in) long
Distribution	North America; Europe; Asia; winters as far S as Africa, Central America
Habitat	Reeded ponds and streams; marshes; sometimes estuaries and coasts
Diet	Aquatic plants and their seeds; small animals (especially in summer)
Breeding	Hollow in ground lined with leaves and down, among reeds; eight to ten eggs, incubated by female for about 21 days

Wood duck

Many bird-lovers regard the North American wood duck, together with its close east Asian relative the Mandarin duck (*Aix galericulata*), to be the most beautiful of all waterfowl. As with most ducks, the female is less colourful than the male but has a distinctive teardrop-shaped white eye patch. Both sexes also usually have a fine crest of feathers on the head. As its name suggests, the wood duck is one of the few ducks that habitually perch on the branches of trees and bushes; it nests in hollow tree-trunks. It was very common in the early 19th century but was hunted almost to extinction; conservation measures allowed populations to recover well.

Scientific name	*Aix sponsa*
Family	Anatidae
Size	43–48cm (17–19in) long
Distribution	North America (mainly E of Mississippi, W of Rockies); winters farther S
Habitat	Woodland (mainly deciduous) with creeks, rivers and lakes; swamps
Diet	Vegetation; seeds; acorns; fruits; young eat mainly aquatic insects
Breeding	Nest a cavity in tree (or man-made nest box) lined with down; 10–15 eggs, incubated by female for 28–30 days

Common eider

Inhabiting wind-buffeted Arctic coasts, the female eider has evolved particularly thick and soft down on her breast that she uses to line the nest and cover the eggs when she is away feeding. For centuries people have collected this down to make quilts – commonly known as eiderdowns. As with most other ducks, the female is mainly brown in colour, with fine black barring. In the breeding season, the male is a much more striking black and white, with greenish patches on the head, but after moulting is mostly black. Like the even more colourful king eider (*Somateria spectabilis*), common eiders up-end or dive into even rough seas for their food.

Scientific name	*Somateria mollissima*
Family	Anatidae
Size	53–70cm (21–27½in) long
Distribution	Northern coasts of Asia, Europe, North America; winters farther S
Habitat	Mainly coasts and islands; sometimes inland rivers and lakes
Diet	Mainly small crustaceans and molluscs
Breeding	Nest of seaweed and grass, lined with down, on rocky or sandy ground; four to six eggs, incubated by female alone for 27–28 days

Hooded merganser

The mergansers and their close relatives – including the goosander (*Mergus merganser*), smew (*M. albellus*) and red-breasted merganser (*M. serrator*) – are unusual fish-eating ducks whose bill is much thinner and more sharply pointed than that of most other ducks, with a hooked tip and tooth-like serrations. These features are adaptations to the birds' diet – which they detect by watching from the surface and catch by diving and swimming rapidly underwater. The male hooded merganser in breeding plumage is the most striking of the group, with its large black-bordered white crest or hood. Females are greyish-brown, also with a crest.

Scientific name	*Mergus cucullatus* or *Lophodytes cucullatus*
Family	Anatidae
Size	40–48cm (16–19in) long
Distribution	Eastern United States and southern Canada; also west of Rockies
Habitat	Forested wetlands (lakes; rivers); often near southern coasts in winter
Diet	Fish, frogs, crayfish and other aquatic invertebrates
Breeding	Nests in hollow tree or nesting box lined with down; usually 10–12 eggs, incubated by female for about 28–33 days

South American king vulture

DNA evidence suggests that the the king vulture and other New World vultures and condors may be more closely related to storks than to the similar-looking vultures of the Old World. For this reason, some ornithologists classify them in a separate order, or major group. If they are right, the similarities must result from convergent evolution – adaptation to similar ways of life. They include broad wings for soaring, a hooked bill for tearing flesh, and a bare head and neck to avoid the feathers being soiled when feeding. The king vulture, as its name suggests, is the top predator in its territory; it can tear the hide of even large prey. It depends a lot on its sense of smell to detect dead meat in the dense jungle.

Scientific name	*Sarcoramphus papa*
Family	Cathartidae or possibly Ciconiidae
Size	76–81cm (30–32in) long
Distribution	Mexico to northern Argentina
Habitat	Tropical forests; sometimes grassland
Diet	Carrion (dead animals and fish); may kill small mammals and reptiles
Breeding	Habits poorly understood; probably one or two eggs, incubated by both sexes

Snail or Everglade kite

Unlike almost all other birds of prey, the snail kite has an extremely specialized diet, eating almost solely the 4cm (1½in) apple snail, which lives in freshwater marshes. As such marshland deteriorated in many areas – such as the Everglades of southern Florida – during the 20th century, snail kite numbers dropped to low levels. The bird is still endangered, but conservation measures (including the preservation of marshes and removal of excess water hyacinth plants, which prevent the birds spotting snails in the water) have allowed its numbers to increase. Like other kites, it is a lightly built bird. It flies low over the water with slow wingbeats, swooping to catch snails with its talons.

Scientific name	*Rostrhamus sociabilis*
Family	Accipitridae
Size	36–40cm (14–16in) long
Distribution	Florida; parts of Caribbean, Mexico, Central America and South America
Habitat	Freshwater marshes
Diet	Freshwater apple snails (*Pomacea paludosa*); sometimes small turtles
Breeding	Nests in colonies. Simple nest of vegetation in marshland grasses or bushes; two to four eggs, incubated by both sexes for 27–28 days

Bald eagle

The United States national bird belongs to the group known as fish or sea eagles, because they feed largely on fish. Bald eagles like river salmon, but their main food is dead or dying fish picked up from the shoreline. They also kill birds and small mammals. They often harass other birds – especially ospreys (*see p.83*) – to force them to drop their catch, which the bald eagle may catch before it hits the water. It is an impressive-looking bird, the 'bald' head being clothed in pure white feathers. But it is endangered. It once bred in many parts of North America, but destruction of wild habitats and the effect of pesticide poisoning mean that it is now common only in Alaska and western Canada.

Scientific name	*Haliaeetus leucocephalus*
Family	Accipitridae
Size	Male 76–86cm (30–34in) long; wingspan up to 2.5m (8ft); female larger
Distribution	Much of North America, but commonest in north-west
Habitat	Wooded country near coast or open water
Diet	Fish (alive or dead); ducks, gulls and other birds; small mammals
Breeding	Pairs mate for years. Nest of sticks up to 2.5m (8ft) across in tree or on rocks; one to three eggs, incubated mainly by female for 34–36 days

White-breasted sea eagle

Sometimes called the white-fronted, or white-bellied, sea eagle, this Asian and Australian bird is a skilled hunter, but like most birds of prey it will also feed on carrion – including dead domestic animals such as lambs. It hunts mainly by swooping down on its prey from a high perch and snatching it from land or water with its talons; it can carry a creature weighing up to about half its own weight. Like the bald eagle, it will harass other birds, such as gannets, for their catch. But if it approaches a nesting colony of gulls, terns or other sociable birds, they are liable to team up to chase the intruder away. It is a protected species in Australia.

Scientific name	*Haliaeetus leucogaster*
Family	Accipitridae
Size	Male about 76cm (30in) long; female about 84cm (33in)
Distribution	India and southern China to New Guinea and Australia
Habitat	Coasts and near rivers and lakes
Diet	Fish; reptiles; ducks and other birds; small or young mammals
Breeding	Very large nest of sticks on tall tree or cliff, or sometimes on ground; usually two eggs, incubated mainly by female for 40–44 days

Egyptian vulture

Sometimes nicknamed Pharaoh's chicken, the Egyptian vulture played an important symbolic part in Ancient Egyptian life – probably because of its long association with humans and its role in disposing of dead creatures – and it appears in many drawings on the walls of Egyptian tombs. It is a relatively small vulture, and has to take second pickings to bigger scavengers at a carcass. But it is one of very few birds to use a 'tool' to get food. It likes to eat ostrich and flamingo eggs, and it may throw the egg with its beak to try to break it open; if this does not work, it will pick up a stone in its beak and throw it at the egg, persisting until the egg cracks.

Scientific name	*Neophron percnopterus*
Family	Accipitridae
Size	Male about 63cm (25in) long; female about 70cm (27½in)
Distribution	Southern Europe; Middle East; India; most of Africa
Habitat	Open country, especially rocky and mountainous; often near humans
Diet	Carrion and refuse; insects; eggs and chicks of ostriches and other birds
Breeding	Nest of sticks lined with fur, dung and other materials on crag, cave or building; one or two eggs, incubated by both sexes for about 42 days

Cinereous vulture

This rather unattractive-looking bird is often called the European or Eurasian black vulture – which may confuse it with the much smaller American black vulture (*Coragyps atratus*) or the Indian black or king vulture (*Sarcogyps calvus*). It is the biggest bird of prey in the Old World, and is the dominant scavenger in its territory, feeding mainly on the flesh and internal organs of large dead animals. It has a huge hooked bill, ideal for tearing the prey's hide and sinews, but its claws are more like toenails than talons. Its vast wings enable it to soar over great distances in search of food – which it can spot from far away with its sharp eyesight.

Scientific name	*Aegypius monachus*
Family	Accipitridae
Size	1–1.1m (3¼–3½ft) long; wingspan up to 2.9m (9½ft)
Distribution	Parts of southern Europe and North Africa; much of Asia (to China)
Habitat	Many types of terrain, including semi-desert, scrub, grassland and forest
Diet	Carrion, mainly from large carcasses; may catch small live prey
Breeding	Large nest of sticks, lined with scavenged materials, usually in tree; usually single egg, incubated for 50–55 days

Crested snake eagle

Snake eagles, or serpent eagles, feed largely on snakes and other reptiles (including dead ones), and their feet are well adapted for grasping their slippery prey. The toes are short and strong, with a rough under-surface. The crested snake eagle is a woodland bird that often perches, motionless, on the branch of a tree, watching for suitable prey; it then swoops down to seize its victim on the ground. The bird is a fine flier, soaring effortlessly above the tree canopy – making loud ringing and screaming calls to its mate – but it rarely hunts from the air. The species lives over a wide area but does not migrate, and there are many local subspecies of differing size and colouring.

Scientific name	*Spilornis cheela*
Family	Accipitridae
Size	Varies from about 50–70cm (20–28in) long
Distribution	Asia from India to southern China, Bali and Philippines
Habitat	Mainly forests and woodland
Diet	Mainly tree and other snakes; lizards; some small mammals; rarely, birds
Breeding	Quite small nest of sticks built in tree; single egg, incubated by female (who is fed by male) for about 35 days

Bateleur

The French name of this bird means 'tumbler' or 'acrobat', and it can perform spectacular aerial manoeuvres – even full somersaults in mid-air – especially during courtship displays. It is a member of the snake-eagle group, and eats reptiles and amphibians, but also carrion. It swoops on its prey from the wing, sometimes from a great height. It has a unique profile in the air, with its very short tail (behind which its feet project) and proportionately extremely long wings. It can soar as well as tumble, but the short tail means that it often swerves from side to side. It roosts in trees at night but spends most of the day on the wing, flying as much as 320km (200 miles) each day. It is an endangered species.

Scientific name	*Terathopius ecaudatus*
Family	Accipitridae
Size	Male 55cm (22in) long; female 70cm (28in); wingspan up to 1.8m (6ft)
Distribution	Most of Africa south of Sahara; south-western Arabia
Habitat	Tropical and subtropical grassland; scrub; open woodland
Diet	Carrion; reptiles and amphibians; small mammals and birds; some fish
Breeding	Quite small cup-shaped nest of twigs; single egg, incubated by female for about 42 days, accompanied by male and often a third adult guard

Hen harrier or marsh hawk

Harriers are rather long-legged birds of prey with a long square tail and long wings. They have owl-like discs around the eyes. The hen or northern harrier – known in North America as the marsh hawk – is one of the most widespread species of a very cosmopolitan group. (There are harriers almost everywhere except Antarctica.) Unusually for a hawk, male and female hen harriers differ in colour as well as size; the male is grey, the female brown. Both have a distinctive white rump patch. Like other harriers, they hunt by gliding backwards and forwards low over the ground. On spotting a vole, mouse or small bird, they turn abruptly with fanned tail and drop to catch it in their talons.

Scientific name	*Circus cyaneus*
Family	Accipitridae
Size	Male about 43cm (17in) long; female about 51cm (20in)
Distribution	Most of North and Central America, Europe and Asia; not India, Arabia
Habitat	Moors; marshland; grassland; fields; sand dunes
Diet	Small mammals and birds; lizards; frogs; large insects
Breeding	Nest of twigs, grass and other materials on ground, sheltered by vegetation; four to six eggs, incubated by female for 32–37 days

Northern goshawk

Goshawks are fierce, aggressive and persistent hunters. They chase and catch birds such as crows, pigeons, grouse and pheasants on the wing or on the ground. They will chase a rabbit through dense undergrowth or a squirrel running from tree to tree. Their hunting prowess has for centuries made them a favourite of falconers, but they are difficult birds to train. Japanese falconers used goshawks to hunt cranes several times the hawk's size. The northern goshawk is the largest of nearly 50 closely related species, all long-tailed, long-legged, fast fliers; the smallest is the African little sparrowhawk (*Accipiter minullus*), only 20cm (8in) long.

Scientific name	*Accipiter gentilis*
Family	Accipitridae
Size	Male about 51cm (20in) long; female 60cm (24in)
Distribution	Almost all temperate regions of Northern Hemisphere
Habitat	Woodland (especially coniferous), often near open country
Diet	Mainly birds up to own size; also mammals up to size of young hare
Breeding	Usually mates for life. Nest a platform of sticks and other materials in tree; usually three or four eggs, incubated by female for 36–38 days

Red-tailed hawk

This species is the commonest and most widespread North American hawk. It is a member of the group known as buteos or buzzards – broad-winged and broad-tailed medium to large hawks that also include the rather similar common buzzard (*Buteo buteo*) of Europe, Asia and Africa. Like other buzzards, the red-tail soars and circles powerfully on its big wings, watching for prey; it is also often seen perching – equally vigilant – on tall trees or telegraph poles. It will swoop on almost any small creature that moves. Some red-tailed hawk populations migrate south in winter, but most have specific territories. About 14 geographical subspecies have been identified, with different markings or colouring.

Scientific name	*Buteo jamaicensis*
Family	Accipitridae
Size	Male about 48cm (19in) long; female 63cm (25in)
Distribution	North and Central America; Caribbean
Habitat	Adaptable: deserts, mountains, forests and swamps
Diet	Rabbits and rodents preferred; also other mammals, birds and reptiles
Breeding	Large nest of sticks, leaves and bark in high tree; up to four or sometimes five eggs, incubated by both sexes for 28–32 days

Harpy eagle

The world's biggest eagle, the harpy is an endangered and rare inhabitant of the Central and South American tropical rainforests. It is the dominant predator of the forest canopy, where it soars between and just below the top of the trees. It is highly manoeuvrable despite its 2.1m (7ft) wingspan, and often chases monkeys through the trees, snatching its prey with its powerful talons. (The claws grow as much as 18cm [7in] long.) It can briefly achieve speeds of 50km/h (30mph) during such a chase. The harpy also eats other mammals, including ground-dwellers such as agouti (a rodent) and small deer, plus porcupines and large birds. The main threat to its survival is human destruction of its habitat.

Scientific name	*Harpia harpyja*
Family	Accipitridae
Size	Male about 90cm (35in) long; female up to 102cm (40in)
Distribution	Central and South America from Mexico to northern Argentina
Habitat	Mainly lowland rainforest
Diet	Mostly arboreal mammals such as monkeys, sloths and opossums
Breeding	Generally breeds every other year. Large nest of sticks in tree, 30–45m
	(100–150ft) above ground; one or two eggs, incubated for 53–56 days

Wedge-tailed eagle

Wedge-tailed eagles are Australia's biggest birds of prey, with wings spanning as much as 2.5m (about 8ft). They belong – together with the closely related golden eagle (*Aquila chrysaetos*) of the northern hemisphere – to the group known as true or booted eagles, which have legs fully clothed in feathers down to the base of the toes. Wedge-tailed eagles are strong fliers, soaring for as long as 1½ hours at a time and reaching heights of 2000m (6500ft). They descend on their ground-living prey in a long, slanting swoop, and eat it on the spot. They have long been hunted by farmers, but they rarely take any stock but weak or already dead lambs or sheep.

Scientific name	*Aquila audax*
Family	Accipitridae
Size	Male about 90cm (35in) long; female 1m (39in)
Distribution	Australia; southern New Guinea
Habitat	Most areas, but especially open woodland with grass ground cover
Diet	Rabbits; wallabies; kangaroos; snakes; lizards; carrion including sheep
Breeding	Pairs for life. Nest a large platform of sticks in fork of tall tree; one to three eggs (usually two), incubated mainly by female for 43–45 days

Osprey

Sometimes called the fish eagle, the osprey is never found very far from fresh or salt water – but that is about its only restriction, for few birds are more widely spread around the world. (In the Southern Hemisphere, however, it breeds only in Australia; elsewhere it is a seasonal visitor.) It eats only fresh or very recently dead fish. It circles up to 60m (200ft) above the water to spot its prey, then swoops and plunges feet-first to grab the fish – often submerging in the process. It struggles to take off again, then carries its meal to a convenient perch to feed. Its feet are well adapted for such fishing, with spiked soles, curved claws and reversible outer toes.

Scientific name	*Pandion haliaetus*
Family	Accipitridae or Pandionidae
Size	Male about 50cm (20in) long; female 58cm (23in)
Distribution	Worldwide except polar regions, southern South America, New Zealand
Habitat	Mainly near coasts; also large inland lakes and rivers
Diet	Fish
Breeding	Very large nest of sticks, lined with seaweed, usually on tall tree or cliff; usually three eggs, incubated mainly by female for 34–36 days

Gyrfalcon

Most falcons have much narrower and more sharply pointed wings than hawks and eagles, and are generally faster fliers. Many specialize in chasing and catching other birds in mid-air, or strike ground-living prey at amazing speed. They include the main species trained by falconers to hunt on command, and one of the most spectacular of all these birds is the gyrfalcon – whose use in the Middle Ages was restricted to royalty. It is the biggest of all falcons, the size of many hawks. Its colour varies with location between almost white – long prized as the most spectacular form – and a dark brown-grey, always with distinctive and beautiful markings. Gyrfalcons mostly hunt close to the ground.

Scientific name	*Falco rusticolus*
Family	Falconidae
Size	Male 50cm (20in) long; female 63cm (25in); wingspan up to 1.6m (5¼ft)
Distribution	Circumpolar arctic and subarctic regions
Habitat	Open country: tundra and mountains
Diet	Birds, especially arctic ptarmigan, grouse and seabirds; small mammals
Breeding	Pairs for life. May use other bird's old nest, but usually nests on bare rock; three or four eggs, incubated mainly by female for 34–36 days

Peregrine falcon

The fastest flier of all birds of prey, the peregrine falcon – sometimes known in the United States as the duck hawk – can achieve speeds of at least 110km/h (70mph) in level flight. Claims for speeds observed in a hunting stoop (dive) range up to 300km/h (190mph) or even more. Whatever the true figure, it is a powerful hunter, striking its prey from a great height fast enough to break its back in one blow. Although not as big as the gyrfalcon, it is a majestic bird that has long been the most popular species among falconers. In the 20th century it was seriously endangered by pesticides (especially DDT), but numbers are slowly recovering.

Scientific name	*Falco peregrinus*
Family	Falconidae
Size	Male 38cm (15in) long; female 53cm (21in)
Distribution	All continents except Antarctica
Habitat	Mountains; coasts; most types of open country; many high-rise cities
Diet	Birds, especially pigeons and gamebirds; sometimes other small animals
Breeding	Nests mainly on high cliff ledges, or sometimes on ground or skyscraper; two to five eggs, incubated mainly by female for 28–34 days

Collared or red-legged falconet

The falconets, or pygmy falcons, are the smallest birds of prey, more or less the size of a sparrow. There are species in Africa and South America, but the closely related species of the genus *Microhierax* all live in southern and south-east Asian forests. The very smallest is the Philippine falconet (*M. erythrogonys*). The collared falconet can be distinguished from the black-legged falconet (*M. fringillarius*) by its leg colour and white forehead, and from the pied falconet (*M. melanoleucus*) by its white collar. All are too small to hunt any but the very smallest birds, lizards and mammals, and these birds all eat mainly dragonflies and other forest insects.

Scientific name	*Microhierax caerulescens*
Family	Falconidae
Size	14–18cm (5½–7in) long
Distribution	Northern India and Nepal to Vietnam and Thailand
Habitat	Mainly open forest with clearings, up to 1700m (5500ft) above sea-level
Diet	Insects; very small birds
Breeding	Nests in old woodpecker or barbet holes in trees, 6–10m (20–30ft) above
	ground; four or five eggs, incubated mainly by female

Secretary bird

The common name of this bird refers to its crest of lax black feathers, which supposedly look like quill pens lodged behind a 19th-century clerk's ear. It is quite distinct from other birds of prey, with its extremely long legs and habit of walking or running on the ground in preference to flying. Yet it has a rather hawk-like body and head. It hunts on foot, picking up small prey with its bill but first killing larger creatures – notably snakes – by stamping on them. When running after prey it often flaps its wings – more to confuse the victim than to add speed. The secretary bird has rather short toes that are good for running but poorly adapted for carrying prey, so it takes food to its young in the tree-top nest in its bill or crop.

Scientific name	*Sagittarius serpentarius*
Family	Sagittariidae
Size	Up to 1.5m (5ft) long; stands about 1m (3ft 3in) tall; wingspan 2m (6½ft)
Distribution	Most of Africa south of Sahara
Habitat	Savannah grasslands and other open country
Diet	Snakes and other reptiles; small mammals and birds; large insects
Breeding	Probably mates for life. Nest a large, rough platform of sticks on low tree or bush; usually two eggs, incubated by both sexes for 42–45 days

Mallee fowl

This distant relative of the domestic chicken has a bizarre method of incubating its eggs shared by other members of the megapode family. The male digs a hole, about 1m (about 3ft) deep and 3–4m (10–13ft) across, into which he scrapes a mound of dry leaves and twigs. Once rain dampens the material, he covers the mound with sandy soil to retain the warmth of the rotting vegetation (and of the sun). When the female wants to lay an egg, he digs a chamber for it. The male spends most of the year tending the mound, opening it when necessary to keep it at about 33°C (91°F) to incubate the eggs. Apart from this, male and female ignore both eggs and chicks.

Scientific name	*Leipoa ocellata*
Family	Megapodidae
Size	About 60cm (24in) long
Distribution	Southern Australia
Habitat	Mallee (dwarf eucalypt scrub) and other semi-arid areas
Diet	Seeds (mostly acacia), plant buds and young shoots; some insects
Breeding	Male builds huge incubation mound and chambers (*see above*); usually 15–24 eggs laid at intervals of 2–17 days; hatch after about seven weeks

Great curassow

The most obvious feature of this large forest bird is the curly crest of feathers on the head of both sexes. In other respects the males and females are distinct. The male's plumage is mainly almost black; it has a yellow protuberance at the base of the bill. The female shows three colour forms in different regions, ranging from reddish-brown to a striped pattern. Although the bird is well adapted to life among forest trees, it spends most of its days rummaging in the leaf litter on the forest floor for fruits and other food. The male has a loud, booming call that carries a great distance – essential for maintaining contact or attracting a mate in the dense forest.

Scientific name	*Crax rubra*
Family	Cracidae
Size	Up to about 1m (3ft 3in) long
Distribution	Americas from southern Mexico to Ecuador
Habitat	Tropical rainforest
Diet	Fruits, berries, seeds and other plant material
Breeding	Untidy nest of twigs built in tree or bush; usually two large eggs, incubated by female for about 30 days

Common or wild turkey

It is believed that the native peoples of Mexico first domesticated the wild turkey which was later taken to Europe by the Spanish in the 16th century. It became an important food for the early European settlers in North America – hence its role on Thanksgiving tables ever since. The wild species still lives in scattered woodland areas. It is a big bird (though slimmer than the domesticated variety) that roosts in trees but feeds and nests on the ground. Males compete to collect harems of females by strutting and displaying their fanned tail in special display grounds called leks, while making a 'gobble-gobble' call. A successful male mates with many females.

Scientific name	*Meleagris gallopavo*
Family	Phasianidae
Size	Male about 1.25m (4ft) long; female about 90cm (3ft)
Distribution	Much of North America, from southern Canada to northern Mexico
Habitat	Woodland: forest clearings and edges
Diet	Seeds; nuts; berries; some insects and lizards
Breeding	Polygynous. Nest a shallow leaf-lined hollow in ground; each female
	lays 8–15 eggs, usually in separate nest, and incubates for about 28 days

Spruce grouse

Nicknamed the 'fool hen' because of its tameness towards humans, the spruce grouse is a stocky, rather chicken-like bird that is sometimes called the spruce hen or spruce chicken. As the name suggests, it is a forest-dweller that is quite common in the northern conifer forests of North America. However, because of logging, it has become rare and even endangered in some areas, such as New York state. The male and female birds are similar, but the female is smaller and browner, and has no red comb over the eyes. As with related bird species, males strut and display their tail feathers to attract females, who nest alone after mating.

Scientific names	Canachites canadensis; Dendragapus canadensis; Falcipennis canadensis
Family	Phasianidae; sometimes classified in separate grouse family, Tetraonidae
Size	38–43cm (15–17in) long; female slightly smaller
Distribution	Parts of northern United States; most of Canada except far north
Habitat	Coniferous forest (especially spruce and pine)
Diet	Tree buds and needles; some insects
Breeding	Polygynous. Nest a hollow in ground lined with moss and leaves, under low branch; usually five or six mottled eggs, incubated for 21–23 days

Mountain or plumed quail

The largest and one of the most striking of the North American quails, the mountain or plumed quail is a plump little bird. It is the only quail of North America in which both male and female have a long, more-or-less straight black plume (a narrow pair of feathers) projecting from the head. Some other species also have a crest, but it curves markedly forward. The chestnut-brown throat also distinguishes it from mostly grey or brown relatives such as the California quail (*Lophortiyx californicus*) – California's state bird – and the bobwhite quail (*Colinus virginianus*), common in eastern and southern North America. All New World quails form sociable groups, or coveys, of 50 or more nesting pairs.

Scientific name	*Oreortyx pictus*
Family	Phasianidae; sometimes classified in separate family, Odontophoridae
Size	26–29cm (10–11½in) long
Distribution	Western North America, from British Columbia to Baja California
Habitat	Mountain coniferous and mixed forest and scrub up to 3000m (10,000ft)
Diet	Seeds, acorns and fruits; soft vegetation; some insects
Breeding	Nest a depression in ground at base of tree or rock, or near bush; seven to ten reddish eggs, incubated mainly by female for 24–25 days

Congo peafowl

The beautiful and rare Congo peafowl was unknown to scientists until the 1930s. American zoologist James Chapin found live specimens in 1935, after years of searching in the jungles of West Africa. Before that, he had seen only feathers of the bird – called *mbulu* by local people – in headdresses, and mislabelled stuffed birds in a museum. The discovery was important because it is the only African member of the pheasant family. (Others are natives of Asia and Europe.) Congo peacocks (the female is called a 'peahen') have a much shorter train than the well-known Indian blue peacock (*Pavo cristatus*). The hen is mostly brown, with metallic green wings.

Scientific name	*Afropavo congogensis*
Family	Phasianidae
Size	63–71cm (25–28in) long; female smaller
Distribution	West Africa (basin of Congo River)
Habitat	Tropical rainforest
Diet	Omnivorous; especially fallen fruits and insects such as termites
Breeding	May nest in trees; two to four light-brown eggs, incubated by female for about 26 days

Satyr tragopan

Most male birds in the pheasant family have beautifully coloured and/or patterned plumage, but few match that of the five tragopan species, natives of the Himalayas. The satyr tragopan is particularly striking, with black-edged white spots, or *ocelli* ('eyes'), scattered over the deep crimson and brownish plumage. The female is a much duller brown. Also called the crimson horned tragopan, the satyr tragopan is named for the fleshy crimson projections, or 'horns', above the eyes that the male inflates as part of his courtship display. (In Greek mythology, satyrs were horned demons.) At the same time, he expands red neck lappets (wattles).

Scientific name	*Tragopan satyra*
Family	Phasianidae
Size	66–71cm (26–28in) long; female smaller
Distribution	Himalayas from Kashmir to central China
Habitat	Mountain forest above about 2450m (8000ft); lower in winter
Diet	Insects; fruits; seeds; leaves; shoots
Breeding	Nests in trees; four to six eggs, incubated by female for about 28 days

Helmeted guineafowl

The helmeted guineafowl – so called because of the horny casque, or helmet-like growth, on its head – is the ancestor of the domesticated guineafowl, which is raised in most parts of the world. (The Ancient Greeks and Romans first introduced it to Europe from Africa.) It is an extremely gregarious bird, living – except in the breeding season – in flocks of as many as 2000 birds. They roost in trees at night, and in the morning come down and move together in single file to a water source to drink. Later they feed together in a broader formation; if threatened by a predator, they form a tight cluster. They run rather than fly from their enemies.

Scientific name	*Numida meleagris*
Family	Numididae
Size	About 63cm (25in) long
Distribution	Originally Africa; introduced to most parts of the world
Habitat	Brushland and forest
Diet	Insects; seeds, leaves and other plant materials
Breeding	Monogamous, but male sometimes mates with other females. Nest a hollow in ground; 10 to 20 eggs, incubated by female for 24–25 days

Hoatzin

The hoatzin has puzzled scientists for centuries. It has long been grouped with the gamebirds because it shares many features with them, but many scientists today believe it is more closely related to cuckoos (order Cuculiformes; *see pp.152–159*). Others put it in an order of its own, Opisthocomiformes. Whatever its classification, it is a strange bird, with a small head and large wings (although it flies poorly), that lives in small flocks. It has an unusually large crop in the chest, which serves part of the function of the gizzard in starting to digest tough leaves. The almost naked chicks can crawl almost as soon as they hatch, using their feet and two wing claws.

Scientific name	*Opisthocomus hoatzin*
Family	Opisthocomidae
Size	About 60cm (24in) long, including tail
Distribution	South America – Amazon and Orinoco River basins
Habitat	Edges of forest bordering rivers, streams and lakes
Diet	Mainly leaves, especially of arum plants and mangroves; some fruits
Breeding	Nest an untidy platform of sticks on branch overhanging river; two or three spotted eggs, probably incubated by both sexes for about 28 days

Barred buttonquail, or bustard quail

Buttonquails are small ground-living birds that from a distance strongly resemble true quails of the pheasant family. Anatomically, however, they resemble other members of the very diverse group that includes cranes and bustards (hence the alternative name). Nevertheless, some scientists believe that the 17 buttonquail species are distinctive enough to be placed in an order of their own, Turniciformes. The most obvious feature is the lack of a hind toe – hence another alternative name, hemipode ('half-foot'). Their polyandrous breeding habits are also distinctive; females initiate courtship and in many species take several mates in a season.

Scientific name	*Turnix suscitator*
Family	Turnicidae
Size	13–15cm (5–6in) long
Distribution	Tropical and subtropical Asia: Pakistan to Indonesia and southern Japan
Habitat	Grassland; scrub; fields; felled forest
Diet	Seeds; insects; vegetation
Breeding	Female initiates courting behaviour. Nest a hollow in ground; three to five eggs, incubated by male for 12–13 days

White-breasted mesite

Mesites are rare birds that live only on the island of Madagascar, off the east coast of southern Africa. There are three species living in different parts of the island, but white-breasted mesites are probably the most seriously endangered, due to widespread destruction of their habitat. They live mainly on the forest floor, but may fly a short distance to perch on low branches if threatened. The brown mesite (*Mesitornis unicolor*) is all-brown, without the white breast and markings of the white-breasted species, and lives in rainforest in eastern Madagascar; the grey-backed Bensch's mesite (*Monias benschii*) inhabits scrubland of the south-west.

Scientific name	*Mesitornis* (or *Mesoenas*) *variegata*
Family	Mesitornithidae
Size	About 25cm (10in) long
Distribution	North-western Madagascar
Habitat	Open dry (deciduous) forest
Diet	Insects; seeds; small fruits
Breeding	Nest a frail platform of sticks in low tree or bush; one to three eggs; incubation data uncertain, but probably incubated mainly by female

Whooping crane

In eastern Asia, the magnificent and elegant cranes are revered symbols of long life and fidelity. (They mate for life and perform elaborate courtship dances.) Unfortunately, in North America the whooping crane is the most famous severely endangered bird species. Never common, numbers dropped to fewer than 20 living birds by 1941, mainly because of drainage of their wetland habitats. They mostly bred in the northern Midwest and Canada, and wintered on the Gulf coast. Today, there are nearly 300 'whoopers' in the wild – including nearly 200 migrating between northern Canada and the Gulf of Mexico and a colony of about 90 non-migratory birds in Florida – and another 100 in captivity.

Scientific name	*Grus americana*
Family	Gruidae
Size	1.2–1.5m (4–5ft) tall
Distribution	North America (*see above*)
Habitat	Large wetland areas
Diet	Omnivorous: eats plants, seeds, insects, frogs and other aquatic animals
Breeding	Mates for life. Nest a flat platform of sticks on the ground; usually two eggs (more in captive breeding), incubated by both sexes for 29–31 days

Limpkin

Named for its hesitant, limping walk, the limpkin looks something like a heron, but it has anatomical and other features in common with both cranes and rails (*see pp.99 & 102*). Its most obvious features are its slender build, with a long neck and legs, its long toes (good for walking on swamp vegetation and mud) and its long, slightly curved bill. The bill is somewhat flattened, and is well adapted for extracting its favourite food – water snails – from their shells. Limpkins are tame and trusting birds, and fly only weakly. They are good to eat, and were almost exterminated in Florida and Georgia until they were given legal protection. They are sometimes called the 'crying bird' because of their wailing call.

Scientific name	*Aramus guarauna*
Family	Aramidae
Size	60–70cm (24–27½in) long
Distribution	Americas from south-eastern United States to Argentina; Caribbean
Habitat	Marshes and swamps
Diet	Water snails; also other molluscs and other small aquatic creatures
Breeding	Shallow nest of sticks and reeds on ground near water, or in low tree; four to eight eggs, incubated by both sexes (period not known)

White-winged trumpeter

The three known species of trumpeters all live in the Amazon jungle. Like the limpkin, they have features intermediate between those of cranes and rails. They are rather hunch-backed, with a long neck and legs but a short bill. They live in large flocks on the jungle floor, flying only when essential and then only for short distances. The name comes from the male's loud call, and some native people tame them as watchkeepers to protect their poultry. The body feathers of the white-winged trumpeter have a bronze and purplish sheen. The other species are the grey-winged (*Psophia crepitans*) and dark-winged (*P. viridis*) trumpeters. They all perform elaborate courtship dances, like cranes.

Scientific name	*Psophia leucoptera*
Family	Psophiidae
Size	About 46cm (18in) long
Distribution	Amazon basin of South America
Habitat	Rainforest
Diet	Fruits; nuts; berries; insects
Breeding	Few details known, but believed to nest on ground, or in trees in wet areas; lays six to ten eggs

Takahé

Believed to have been extinct for a century until a colony of about 400 birds was discovered in isolated mountain valleys in New Zealand in 1948, the takahé is still highly endangered. It looks rather like a very heavily built gallinule or moorhen – closely related rail species of Eurasia, Africa and the Americas – and they probably evolved from very similar ancestors. Isolated in its island home and with few enemies, the takahé eventually grew heavier, with a bill adapted to cutting tough grass shoots, and lost the power of flight. Then European settlers introduced weasels, stoats and other predators – and red deer that competed for the takahé's food – and the bird was driven to the brink of extinction.

Scientific name	*Notornis* (or *Porphyrio*) *mantelli*
Family	Rallidae
Size	About 63cm (25in) long
Distribution	South-western South Island of New Zealand
Habitat	Alpine grassland at 750–1200m (2500–4000ft)
Diet	Shoots and seeds of grasses; fern roots in winter
Breeding	Usually mates for life. Nest a grass-lined hollow in ground (built after several trial nests); two eggs, incubated by both sexes for 28–30 days

African finfoot

With its streamlined body and fleshily lobed toes (the origin of its name) to act as paddles, the African finfoot is an adept swimmer and diver. It may ride high in the water, or compress its feathers to reduce buoyancy and swim half-submerged. It superficially resembles a grebe (*see pp.30–31*), and carries its young on its back grebe-fashion; it is sometimes called a sun-grebe, but the species are not related. It is a secretive bird that takes cover in thick undergrowth when disturbed. The female is more brightly coloured, though smaller, than the male, with whitish throat feathers instead of grey, and is believed to play the dominant courtship role.

Scientific name	*Podica senegalensis*
Family	Heliornithidae
Size	Male about 63cm (25in) long; female 50cm (20in)
Distribution	Much of Africa south of Sahara, except south-west
Habitat	Mangrove swamps; wooded waterways
Diet	Fish, insects and other small aquatic creatures; some vegetation
Breeding	Nest of twigs and vegetation in dense undergrowth or on branch overhanging water; usually two eggs; other details uncertain

Kagu

In a group containing many diverse members, the kagu is another anomaly that seems to have no very close relatives. The only member of its family, it inhabits the Pacific island of New Caledonia, off Australia's north-east coast. It is a squat, strong-legged, mainly nocturnal bird with a sharp, powerful bill well adapted for probing the ground for small creatures to eat. It can hardly fly, but pairs use their wings in elaborate courtship displays. Like other ground-living island species (such as the takahé; *see p.102*), it has become seriously endangered because of the destruction of habitats and competition from introduced dogs, cats, pigs and rats.

Scientific name	*Rhynochetos jubatus*
Family	Rhynochetidae
Size	About 56cm (22in) long
Distribution	New Caledonia
Habitat	Forested mountains
Diet	Worms, grubs, insects and other small creatures
Breeding	Nest of sticks and vegetation on ground; single spotted and blotched pale brown egg, incubated by both sexes for about 36 days

Sunbittern

The sunbittern is another unusual member of the crane and rail group – the only member of its family, and probably most closely related to the kagu. Unlike the kagu, it is a good and graceful flier, although it is most often seen walking on a riverbank or wading in shallow water, searching for food. Its striped plumage gives it good camouflage, but if threatened and unable to escape by flight, it may spread and display its superbly patterned wings (which are black, brown, white, yellow and olive, with a prominent 'eye' spot) and tail feathers in a threatening posture. Both male and female make similar displays as part of their courtship ritual.

Scientific name	*Eurypyga helias*
Family	Eurypygidae
Size	About 46cm (18in) long
Distribution	Central and South America from central Mexico to Brazil
Habitat	Tropical forests near waterways, up to 1000m (3300ft)
Diet	Fish, crustaceans, insects and other small creatures
Breeding	Bulky nest of vegetation and mud on low branch of tree; usually two grey eggs with reddish spots, incubated by both sexes for about 28 days

Crested or red-legged seriema

The crested seriema (or cariama) is a good example of convergent evolution in birds. It looks somewhat like the secretary bird of Africa (*see p.87*) – to which it is completely unrelated – and fills a similar ecological niche (that is, it plays a similar part in the life of its environment). Like the secretary bird, it is a fast-running, mainly ground-living bird that eats small snakes among other small animals. It even has a crest of feathers, rather like the secretary bird's, on its head. Its closest relation is in fact the New Caledonia kagu (*see p.104*). The crested and Burmeister's seriemas (*Chunga bermeisteri*) are the sole descendants of a group of South American carnivorous birds that grew up to 2.5m (8ft) tall.

Scientific name	*Cariama cristata*
Family	Cariamidae
Size	About 76cm (30in) long
Distribution	South America – Brazil and eastern Bolivia to northern Argentina
Habitat	Dry grasslands
Diet	Small animals (insects; frogs; snakes; lizards; rodents) and plant material
Breeding	Nest of sticks on ground or in branches of tree or bush; two or three brown-streaked white eggs, incubated by both sexes for about 26 days

White-bellied bustard

Bustards in flight look rather like long-necked geese, with their strong wing–beats, but they can be easily told apart by the long legs trailing behind the tail and the strange tail-down posture. They are generally bulky birds; the great bustard (*Otis tarda*) of Asia, Europe and north-west Africa is one of the heaviest of all flying birds, weighing up to 17kg (37lb). They have sturdy legs on which they can run at speed in their flat grassland habitat, while their long neck enables them to see over the grass. They usually roam in small flocks and run from threats; but they may hide among the grass stems, well camouflaged by the markings on their mainly brown plumage. Males perform elaborate courtship displays.

Scientific name	*Eupodotis senegalensis*
Family	Otididae
Size	About 53cm (21in) long
Distribution	Much of Africa south of Sahara
Habitat	Dry grassland and scrub
Diet	Omnivorous: eats plants and seeds, also insects and other small animals
Breeding	Nest a bare scrape in ground; one or two eggs, incubated by female for about 25 days

African jaçana, or lilytrotter

This bird's most distinctive feature is its elongated toes and claws, which are an adaptation for walking (or 'trotting') on waterlilies, water hyacinths and other floating plants. It does this with great confidence. In other ways, the bird looks like a long-legged coot, moorhen or gallinule, complete with a fleshy shield above the bill. It has rounded wings with a sharp horny spur, and flies with neck extended and long legs trailing. The name jaçana (pronounced YASSanAH, with a soft 'C' and the stress on the first and last syllables) was adopted by the Spanish from the name used by native Amazon peoples. Seven jaçana species live on all the warm continents.

Scientific name	*Actophilornis africana*
Family	Jacanidae
Size	30cm (12in) long
Distribution	Africa south of Sahara
Habitat	Tropical and subtropical still waterways with floating leaves or plants
Diet	Aquatic insects, small molluscs and fish; seeds of water plants
Breeding	Nest a loose floating mass of vegetation; usually four dark brown
	blotched eggs, incubated mainly by male for about 24 days

Greater painted snipe

The name is apt, at least as far as the female is concerned, for she has beautifully coloured and patterned plumage. This is displayed to greatest effect, showing the spotted pattern on the wings, during courtship flights to attract males (which are duller in colouring) to a territory that she has established, and when she woos her partner by spreading her wings and circling him. She wards off competing females with a warning display that also exposes the wings. After mating, the male builds a nest and incubates the eggs while the female leaves to look for another mate. The South American lesser painted snipe (*Rostratula semicollaris*) is monogamous.

Scientific name	*Rostratula benghalensis*
Family	Rostratulidae
Size	About 25cm (10in) long; male slightly smaller than female
Distribution	Parts of Africa south of Sahara, southern Asia and Australia
Habitat	Muddy swamps and marshland
Diet	Worms, crustaceans and other small creatures; some plant food
Breeding	Usually polyandrous. Nest a mass of reeds and other vegetation (semi-floating or on ground); usually four eggs, incubated by male for 19 days

Crab plover

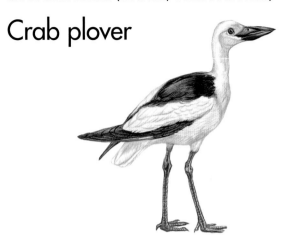

Crab plovers behave very much like other waders as they run about the seashore in noisy flocks, stabbing at prey. Their internal anatomy is also plover-like, but their huge, powerful bill – more like that of a tern (*see p.126*) than of closer relatives – sets them apart, and they are classified in a family of their own. The bill is an adaptation to their diet of crabs and other shellfish; they use it to prise open or break the shell. Crab plovers are mostly nocturnal, feeding on fiddler crabs that emerge at dusk. They are unique among shorebirds – and extremely unusual for such a long-legged species – in nesting at the end of a long burrow dug in the sand.

Scientific name	*Dromas ardeola*
Family	Dromadidae
Size	About 38cm (15in) long
Distribution	Coasts of Indian Ocean, Red Sea and Gulf, South Africa to Andaman Is
Habitat	Sandy beaches and dunes; reefs; mudflats; estuaries
Diet	Crabs, molluscs and other seashore invertebrates
Breeding	Breeds in large colonies, sometimes of thousands. Nest a bare chamber at end of tunnel up to 2m (6½ft) long in sand; usually single egg

Black oystercatcher

Oystercatchers are noisy birds that live on almost all rocky shores worldwide, but ornithologists disagree on how many species there are. Most lists name 10 to 12, but some experts believe they are all variants of one worldwide species while others say there are up to 20. They are certainly all very similar, with either all-black or pied (black and white) plumage, pink to red legs, a red to orange bill, and yellow eyes with an orange ring around them. The bill is flattened at the tip, and is ideal for prising open oyster and other shells; the bird then uses it to cut the muscle by which the mollusc holds its shell closed, and feeds on the contents at its leisure.

Scientific name	*Haematopus bachmanii*
Family	Haematopodidae
Size	About 38cm (15in) long
Distribution	West coast of North America (Alaska to Baja California)
Habitat	Shores and estuaries, especially where rocky
Diet	Shellfish and some other marine invertebrates
Breeding	Nest a hollow (natural or scraped) in ground; two to four eggs, incubated by both sexes for 24–29 days

American avocet

A large, long-legged bird, the American avocet (like avocet species in other parts of the world) has a long upward-curving bill. It feeds while wading in shallow water, sweeping the bill – held partially open – back and forth at the surface or near the bottom. In this way, it catches small aquatic creatures, including the tiny brine shrimps that live in highly salty lakes. The American avocet's size, shape and colouring – especially its pale blue legs and orange-brown tint of its head and neck (most prominent in the breeding season) make it easy to identify. The related stilts of the genus *Himantopus* have a straight bill and proportionately even longer legs.

Scientific name	*Recurvirostra americana*
Family	Recurvirostridae
Size	40–50cm (16–20in) long
Distribution	North America except north-east and far north; winters farther south
Habitat	Shallow fresh or salt water: mudflats, marshes, estuaries and sandbanks
Diet	Small aquatic invertebrates; some small fish and amphibians; seeds
Breeding	Breeds in small colonies. Nest a scrape in ground, sometimes lined with leaves; three to five eggs, incubated by both sexes for 22–29 days

Stone curlew

Knobbly leg joints (actually their heels) give the stone curlews their alternative name of thick-knees. The Eurasian species is the only member of the family to migrate systematically southwards in winter. Although undoubtedly a wader by evolution and anatomy, it is rarely seen in the estuaries and mudflats that other wading birds frequent. It prefers dry, sandy or even stony country (hence the common name), in which its streaked plumage gives it good camouflage. Stone curlews are strong fliers, but spend most of the day crouched on the ground, usually running if disturbed. They become active at dusk, using their big eyes to spot food.

Scientific name	*Burhinus oedicnemus*
Family	Burhinidae
Size	About 40cm (16in) long
Distribution	Western Europe to central Asia, north-west Africa and south-east Asia
Habitat	Open country, especially if rough, dry or stony; farmland to semi-desert
Diet	Snails, worms and other small invertebrates
Breeding	Nest a hollow in ground; usually two eggs, incubated mainly by female (guarded by male) for 26–27 days

Indian courser

Rather like small, very long-legged plovers (*see p.116*) in appearance, coursers are waders that never wade, for their home is the dry, sandy regions of Africa and Asia. The Indian courser was once widespread, but has become scarce in most areas. It has beautiful colouring that gives it good camouflage in its parched habitat. It lives mainly on the ground, 'coursing' (running) around and stopping whenever it spots food – or to stretch upright on its toes, neck extended, to scan its surroundings. It usually crouches to the ground when threatened, but can fly fast when necessary. The even rarer Jourdan's courser (*Rhinoptilus bitorquatus*) of south-eastern India has striking body stripes.

Scientific name	*Cursorius coromandelicus*
Family	Glareolidae
Size	About 23cm (9in) long
Distribution	India; Sri Lanka
Habitat	Dry plains and semi-desert
Diet	Mainly insects
Breeding	Nest a hollow or scrape in ground; usually two or three eggs, incubated (or shaded from sun during day) mainly by female

Spur-winged plover

A short spur on the bend of each wing gives this bird (also called the spur-winged lapwing) its name, but the most obvious feature is its handsome black, white and sandy-brown colouring. It feeds in characteristic plover-fashion, running about the ground and pausing frequently to look for small creatures, which it disturbs by scratching the earth. Males defend their territory and mate with a high-stepping display in which they rise up to full height, spread their wings to show off the spurs, and sometimes run head-down at an opponent. The larger spur-winged (or masked) plover of Australasia and south-east Asia is a different species, *Vanellus miles*.

Scientific name	*Hoplopterus* (or *Vanellus*) *spinosus*
Family	Charadriidae
Size	26–28cm (10–11in) long
Distribution	South-east Europe to Kenya, and across northern sub-Saharan Africa
Habitat	Usually dry open country near water; also marshland, lagoons and fields
Diet	Mostly insects and other small invertebrates; small lizards
Breeding	Nest a simple hollow or scrape in ground; usually four eggs, incubated by both sexes for about 24 days

American or lesser golden plover

Three golden plover species – all similar in appearance – inhabit various parts of the world. Apart from the American species, they are the Pacific golden plover (*Pluvialis fulva*) and the slightly larger Eurasian species (*P. apricaria*). All breed mainly in the far north (the Pacific species in eastern Siberia and western Alaska, the Eurasian as far south as Scotland) but migrate to warmer climes in winter – the American species to South America, the Pacific to Australasia, and the Eurasian to southern and western Europe. The closely related grey plover (*P. squatarola*) is black and white, breeds throughout the Arctic, and similarly migrates to the south.

Scientific name	*Pluvialis dominica*
Family	Charadriidae
Size	About 26cm (10in) long
Distribution	Breeds in far northern North America; winters in South America
Habitat	Tundra; marshes; mudflats; grassland; fields
Diet	Worms, insects and other small creatures
Breeding	Nest a hollow in ground lined with moss or grass; usually four eggs, incubated by both sexes for about 25 days

Ruff

Few if any birds show such marked differences between males and females as this. Apart from size, they are fairly similar outside the breeding season, with mainly mottled brown and black plumage, and look much like other waders. But in the breeding season males develop long ear tufts and an elaborate ruff, or collar; these may be of various colours ranging from white to red, brown and black. Males gather in meeting grounds called leks, and parade, strut, engage in mock-fights and make other displays to attract females. Dark-ruffed males are generally dominant, but tolerate the presence of others to attract females. After mating, a female (called a 'reeve') makes a nest and incubates her eggs alone.

Scientific name	*Philomachus pugnax*
Family	Scolopacidae
Size	Male 26–32cm (10–12½in) long; female 20–25cm (8–10in)
Distribution	Breeds Europe, Siberia; winters Europe, Africa, southern Asia, Australia
Habitat	Tundra; marshes; water-meadows; grassland
Diet	Insects, worms and other small land and aquatic creatures; seeds
Breeding	Polygynous. Nest a grass-lined hollow in ground, generally hidden among grasses; usually four eggs, incubated by female for 20–23 days

Tahitian or bristle-thighed curlew

Despite its name, the rare Tahitian curlew nests exclusively on the upland tundra of northern Alaska. But when winter approaches it begins a 10 000km (6000 mile) migration to Tahiti, Hawaii and other Pacific islands. The bird resembles several other curlew species, such as the whimbrel (*Numenius phaeopus*), which occurs almost worldwide, and the common curlew (*N. arquata*) of Europe, Asia and Africa. It has a similar down-curved bill, with which it probes the shoreline for food, and similar plumage except for the rusty-coloured rump and tail. The name bristle-thighed curlew refers to small bristle-like feathers on the upper legs.

Scientific name	*Numenius tahitiensis*
Family	Scolopacidae
Size	About 48cm (19in) long
Distribution	Alaska south to Pacific islands
Habitat	Breeding: upland tundra; wintering: rocky and sandy shores and atolls
Diet	Insects; molluscs; crabs; seabirds' eggs; plant material
Breeding	Breeds in loose colonies. Nest a hollow in ground; usually four eggs, incubated by both sexes for about 27 days

Wilson's phalarope

Phalaropes are smaller and
daintier than most waders.
They are also better swimmers,
just as likely to be seen floating
high on the water, or swimming in
small circles picking food from
the surface, as they are wading in
the shallows. Wilson's phalarope
is, however, the least aquatic of
the three species. It also breeds
farther south than the red or grey
phalarope (*Phalaropus
fulicarius*; the two names reflect
its different breeding and winter
colouring) and the northern or
red-necked species (*P. lobatus*) –
which both breed in the Arctic
and winter off coasts to the south.
In all species, the female is bigger,
has more colourful breeding
plumage, and initiates courtship.
The male tends eggs and young.

Scientific name	*Phalaropus tricolor*
Family	Phalaropodidae; sometimes incuded in Scolopacidae
Size	Male about 22cm (8½in) long; female about 24cm (9½in)
Distribution	North America (especially central plains); winters South America
Habitat	Muddy swamps, marshes and shores; other waterways (mainly inland)
Diet	Small aquatic creatures
Breeding	Cup-shape nest built mainly by male on ground among grasses or reeds
	near water; usually four eggs, incubated by male for about 21 days

Patagonian, piping or least seedsnipe

Seedsnipes are South American waders that have adapted to an inland lifestyle, feeding mostly on seeds and other plant material. Their cryptic patterning and behaviour are rather like those of small game birds such as partridges. They are plump little birds, with short legs, pointed wings and a stout, conical, sharp-pointed bill. They live mainly on the ground in small flocks, running around with head forward in search of food; if threatened, they squat on the ground, stationary, and only take flight at the last moment. They fly rapidly and erratically in a zig-zag. The male Patagonian seedsnipe has a characteristic black and white breast pattern.

Scientific name	*Thinocorus rumicivorus*
Family	Thinocoridae
Size	About 18cm (7in) long
Distribution	South America – Ecuador and Bolivia to southern Chile and Argentina
Habitat	Grasslands at high and low altitudes
Diet	Mainly seeds, buds and other vegetation; some insects
Breeding	Nest a shallow hollow in ground; usually four spotted eggs, incubated by female for about 25 days; covers eggs with soil when she leaves nest

Snowy or yellow-billed sheathbill

The name sheathbill refers to the horny or comb-like covering on the top of the bird's bill, partially protecting the nostrils. The snowy sheathbill has pure white plumage. It is a stocky bird about the size of a pigeon, and is a bold scavenger. It can fly and swim well, but it is most likely to be seen on the ground, especially hovering near a penguin, cormorant or other seabird colony, waiting for the opportunity to dash in and steal an egg or small chick; it will also eat carrion and whatever else it can find on the seashore. There are only two species of sheathbill; the black-billed species (*Chionis minor*) lives on the Indian Ocean sector of Antarctica, farther east.

Scientific name	*Chionis alba*
Family	Chionididae
Size	About 40cm (16in) long
Distribution	Antarctic and subantarctic coasts and islands; winters South America
Habitat	Rocky coasts
Diet	Scavenges seabird eggs and chicks; also shoreline creatures and weeds
Breeding	Untidy nest on rocks or in crevice; two or three blotched eggs, incubated by both sexes for about 28 days

Great skua

Skuas are the best-known bird pirates of the oceans, getting much of their food by harrying other seabirds and forcing them to disgorge their catch. The great skua (known in North America simply as the skua) is the biggest of the family, and also takes other birds' eggs, kills nestlings and even adult birds such as gulls and ducks, catches its own fish, and scavenges from fishery factory ships. If, as most experts believe, the Antarctic and smaller northern populations are subspecies of the same species, the great skua is unique in breeding in both the Arctic and Antarctic. The northern population probably originated with southern birds blown off course.

Scientific name	*Stercorarius* (or *Catharacta*) *skua*
Family	Stercorariidae; sometimes included in Lariidae
Size	About 58cm (23in) long
Distribution	Southern and far North Atlantic oceans; winters in warmer latitudes
Habitat	Polar and subpolar coasts; coastal and oceanic waters
Diet	Fish (*see above*); eggs and young of seabirds; other birds; carrion
Breeding	Nests in colonies, usually near other seabirds; nest a grass-lined hollow in ground; usually two eggs, incubated by both sexes for 26–28 days

Long-tailed skua or jaeger

In North America, the smaller members of the skua family are known as jaegers, after the German word for 'hunter'. They do 'hunt' fish and small mammals such as lemmings, but like their bigger cousins they often rob other seabirds of their catch. The long-tailed species is much more lightly built than the great skua, and is almost as long only because adults have long tail feathers. It is predominantly grey rather than brown in colour. Like other members of the family, it is a strong, fast flier that can cover huge distances. It breeds farther north than any other skua, and may venture almost as far as the North Pole, yet winters far south of the Equator.

Scientific name	*Stercorarius longicaudus*
Family	Stercorariidae; sometimes included in Lariidae
Size	About 55cm (22in) long, including long tail feathers
Distribution	Breeds in Arctic (circumpolar); winters throughout Atlantic and Pacific
Habitat	Arctic and subarctic coasts and islands; coastal and oceanic waters
Diet	Fish (mostly by piracy); small mammals; seabird eggs and nestlings
Breeding	Nest a moss, lichen or grass-lined hollow; usually two eggs, incubated by both sexes for 23–28 days

Herring gull

Herring gulls, with their yodelling calls, are among the most familiar of seaside birds in the Northern Hemisphere, and are certainly the commonest coastal gulls in Europe and North America. They are also increasingly common inland, even at great distances from the sea. The secret of their success is their adaptability and opportunism. They prefer to nest on cliffs or dunes, but if necessary will build a nest in a tree or on a building. They prefer fish and animal food if available, but will eat almost anything – from dead fish on the beach to edible garbage on a municipal tip or sewage outlet. The one place these 'seagulls' rarely venture is far out to sea.

Scientific name	*Larus argentatus*
Family	Lariidae
Size	56–66cm (22–26in) long
Distribution	Almost all of Northern Hemisphere; winters in southern part of range
Habitat	Coasts; estuaries; inland waterways; fields; garbage tips
Diet	Surface-living fish; waste; young birds; small animals; worms
Breeding	Nests in colonies on cliffs, dunes and buildings; shallow nest of any available plant material; two or three eggs, incubated for 25–27 days

Swallow-tailed gull

The swallow-tailed gull of the Galápagos and a few other eastern Pacific tropical islands is the world's only nocturnal gull. It leaves its lava-cliff roosts at dusk to feed out at sea. Many fish and squid move close to the surface at night, so are easier to catch. Swallow-tailed gulls have large and very light-sensitive eyes for spotting food, and some experts have suggested that their red eye-rings may help them in some way to spot the phosphorescence – faint light – created by marine creatures. Another advantage of night feeding is that the gulls avoid robber frigate birds (*see p.45*). They may wander over a wide area of the eastern Pacific when not breeding.

Scientific name	*Creagrus* (or *Larus*) *furcatus*
Family	Lariidae
Size	About 38–40cm (15–16in) long
Distribution	Galápagos Islands; eastern Pacific off South American coast
Habitat	Islands; coasts; coastal waters
Diet	Fish and squid
Breeding	Breeds any time of year, at intervals of 9–12 months; nests on cliff, in rock niche or under bush; single egg, incubated by both sexes

Common tern

Terns are members of the same family as gulls, but are far more graceful and lightly built. The common tern's species name *hirundo* is also the scientific name of the swallow (*see p.230*), and refers to the bird's forked tail. However, two other species – the Arctic tern (*Sterna paradisaea*) and roseate tern (*S. dougallii*) – both have a very similar tail and plumage, with a black head and a grey and white body, and bird-watchers often confuse them. Common terns breed in huge colonies and big flocks migrate southwards each winter. The birds are usually seen flying over water – salt or fresh – hovering, and then plunge-diving to catch their prey.

Scientific name	*Sterna hirundo*
Family	Lariidae
Size	31–36cm (12–14in) long
Distribution	Breeds throughout Northern Hemisphere; winters south of Equator
Habitat	Coasts and coastal waters; islands; inland waterways
Diet	Fish, prawns and other marine creatures
Breeding	Pairs for life, returning to same nesting site in colony; nest a hollow in ground; two or three eggs, incubated by both sexes for 21–26 days

Royal tern

In spite of the scientific name *maxima*, this is not the largest species of tern; it is about one-fifth smaller than the Caspian tern (*Sterna caspia*). It is an elegant bird with a large orange bill, black crest of feathers on its head and forked tail – but is less slim in body and bill than the otherwise similar elegant tern (*S. elegans*), which inhabits some of the same parts of the Americas. The royal tern has widespread populations on warm Pacific and Atlantic coasts of the Americas (north of the Equator) and West Africa, but is rare inland. It flies high and fast, plunging from a height of 5–10m (15–30ft) to catch its food, but sometimes also feeds on the surface.

Scientific name	*Sterna maxima* (or *Thalasseus maximus*)
Family	Lariidae
Size	45–53cm (18–21in) long
Distribution	Coasts of southern North America; Caribbean; West Africa
Habitat	Coasts and shallow seas
Diet	Fish and other marine creatures
Breeding	Nests in large colonies on sandy islets and beaches; nest a shallow scrape; usually single egg, incubated by both sexes for 30–31 days

Black skimmer

Skimmer is a very apt name for this bird, for it has a unique method of feeding by skimming along the water surface with its bill open. The lower mandible – which is 2–3cm (about 1in) longer than the upper – cuts through the water to scoop up small fish, shrimps and other items. As soon as it encounters something edible, the bill clamps shut, grabbing the food in one movement or flipping it into the air to catch it before it hits the water. The bird's neck muscles are extra-strong to take the impact of the catch, and it flies with wings high to keep them well clear of the water surface. The technique works well only in calm water, so skimmers are mostly seen in inlets and backwaters, and fish in the evening and at night.

Scientific name	*Rhynchops niger*
Family	Rhynchopidae
Size	46–51cm (18–20in) long; female smaller than male
Distribution	Southern California and Massachusetts to Chile and Argentina
Habitat	Coasts and major rivers and lakes
Diet	Small fish and other marine creatures
Breeding	Breeds in colonies on isolated beaches and sandbanks; nest a scrape in sand; two to five eggs, incubated mainly by female for 23–25 days

Tufted puffin

With its big, colourful bill and display tufts in the breeding season, and its rolling, waddling walk, the tufted puffin and its North Atlantic counterpart the common puffin (*Fratercula arctica*) are among the most comical-looking of birds. They are similar in many ways to penguins (*see pp.20–28*), and fill much the same ecological niche. The biggest difference is that, unlike penguins, puffins can fly – and do so fast and low over the water. Like penguins, however, puffins 'fly' underwater when chasing small fish for their and their young's food. Tufted puffins are common in Alaska, nesting in huge colonies. They use their bill to dig burrows.

Scientific name	*Fratercula* (or *Lunda*) *cirrhata*
Family	Alcidae
Size	About 38cm (15in) long
Distribution	Northern North Pacific; Bering Sea; Sea of Okhotsk
Habitat	Breeds on Asian and American coasts; winters at sea
Diet	Fish and other marine creatures
Breeding	Nest a 1–1.2m (3–4ft) burrow dug in grassy slope, or hollow in rock crevice; one roundish egg, incubated mainly by female for about 41 days

Razorbill

A long, knife-like black and white bill – almost as deep as a puffin's (*see p.129*), but longer – gives the razorbill its name. Of all the auk family, it is the closest in appearance to one of the most famous extinct bird species, the 75cm (30in) great auk (*Pinguinus impennis*). The last pair of great auks (originally called penguins) were killed for food by sailors, and their eggs destroyed, on an Icelandic island in 1844; they now exist only as museum specimens. Razorbills have rather weak legs and webbed feet that are not very good for walking on land but propel them well when swimming on the surface of the sea. They use their wings flipper-fashion (like puffins and penguins) when chasing fish for food underwater.

Scientific name	*Alca torda*
Family	Alcidae
Size	About 40cm (16in) long
Distribution	Northern North Atlantic; sometimes as far south as Mediterranean
Habitat	Cliffs and rocky coasts and coastal waters; winters at sea
Diet	Mostly fish; some other marine creatures
Breeding	Breeds in large colonies on cliffs and rocks; usually single egg laid in protective rock crevice or under boulder; incubated for about 25 days

Guillemot, or common murre

Except for its narrow bill, the guillemot – known in North America as the common murre (rhyming with 'fur') – looks very much like its cousin the razorbill. The two birds also often roost, breed and feed in close proximity where their ranges overlap in the Atlantic; unlike the razorbill, the guillemot is also found in the northern Pacific. It dives for its food like other auks, and breeds in denser colonies than any other bird; as many as 70 pairs have been counted in 1m² (about 10sq ft). It has very variable egg colour – perhaps so parents can recognize their egg in the crowd. The black guillemot (*Cepphus grylle*) is a smaller bird, all black in summer; it stands less upright and may be mistaken for a duck.

Scientific name	*Uria aalge*
Family	Alcidae
Size	38–45cm (15–18in) long
Distribution	Northern North Atlantic and Pacific Oceans
Habitat	Cliffs and rocky coasts and coastal waters; winters at sea
Diet	Fish, molluscs and other marine creatures
Breeding	Breeds in colonies on cliffs and rocks, often close to razorbills; single pear-shaped egg laid on ledge, incubated by both sexes for 28–30 days

Lichtenstein's sandgrouse

DNA evidence suggests that sandgrouse are more closely related to waders than to pigeons, with which they have long been classified. Some scientists put them in an order of their own, Pteroclidiformes. They are unrelated to grouse (*see p.91*), but have a rather grouse-like body and pigeon-like head and neck. Despite living in arid surroundings, they surprisingly eat almost solely dry seeds picked up from the ground with grit that helps to break up the seeds in their gizzard. They need to drink only every one to three days, flying up to 30km (20 miles) to gather in large flocks at waterholes. Lichtenstein's sandgrouse drinks only at dusk or before dawn.

Scientific name	*Pterocles lichtensteinii*
Family	Pteroclidae
Size	About 25cm (10in) long
Distribution	Scattered areas of Africa and Asia from Morocco to Pakistan
Habitat	Semi-desert areas
Diet	Almost entirely small dry seeds, taken with grit; some insects and snails
Breeding	Nest a bare hollow in ground; two or sometimes three eggs, incubated by both sexes for about 25 days

Pin-tailed sandgrouse

Pin-tailed sandgrouse, like the other species, have beautifully patterned back plumage that camouflages them well in their arid, stony, sparsely vegetated habitat. When threatened they crouch low to the ground, but are fast, straight fliers. They feed on the ground, walking with short steps and pecking frequently at seeds. As with other sandgrouse, they generally nest well away from sources of water, and have to fly regularly to waterholes. The pin-tailed sandgrouse is one of the species that drinks in the morning. After the chicks have hatched, the male plunges into the water, which soaks into special feathers on his belly; the chicks drink from this.

Scientific name	*Pterocles alchata*
Family	Pteroclidae
Size	31–39cm (12–15in) long
Distribution	South-west Europe and North Africa to Middle East, central Asia, India
Habitat	Flat, dry country with sparse vegetation
Diet	Mostly small dry seeds, taken with grit; some insects and snails
Breeding	Nest a bare hollow in ground; two or sometimes three eggs, incubated by both sexes for about 25 days

Rock dove

Billions of feral (semi-wild) pigeons in towns and cities worldwide – together with specially bred domestic messenger, racing and fancy pigeons of various colours (including white 'doves') – are all ultimately descended from the rock dove. These descendants are so common that truly wild rock doves that have not interbred with domestic and feral pigeons live only in relatively isolated areas of mountains and cliffs. The prominent black wing bars and the white patch on the pale grey lower back distinguish them from otherwise similar species such as the darker grey, pink-breasted stock dove (*Columba oenas*) and the much larger wood pigeon (*opposite*).

Scientific name	*Columba livia*
Family	Columbidae
Size	31–34cm (12–13in) long
Distribution	Wild: western Europe and North Africa to central Asia, India, Sri Lanka
Habitat	Rocky coasts; cliffs; mountains; deserts; ferals birds in towns worldwide
Diet	Grains and other seeds; berries; some other plant matter; snails
Breeding	Breeds at any time of year. Flimsy nest of twigs on cliff ledge or hole, building or sometimes tree; two eggs, incubated for 17–18 days

Wood pigeon

Nearly as common within its range as the feral pigeon (*see opposite*), the wood pigeon is another opportunist that has spread widely from its original habitat of deciduous and conifer woodland to fields and gardens. In towns and suburbs, wood pigeons often mix with feral pigeons but are easily distinguished by their size and stout build, and by their white wing and neck patches. Even when they cannot be seen, their familiar, endlessly repeated cooing call – with the emphasis usually on the second 'coo' – betrays their presence. When disturbed, wood pigeons 'explode' noisily from their roost on a tree branch and fly off with loud wing-claps.

Scientific name	*Columba palumbus*
Family	Columbidae
Size	40–43cm (16–17in) long
Distribution	Europe; North Africa; Middle East to northern India and Bangladesh
Habitat	Woodland; gardens; farmland
Diet	Seeds; acorns; beechmast; berries; buds
Breeding	May raise three broods a year. Builds shallow twiggy nest hidden high in leafy tree; usually two eggs, incubated by both sexes for 17–18 days

Palm or laughing dove

Known also as the Senegal dove (although it also lives in many other parts of Africa), this bird is a member of the turtle-dove group. The name laughing dove comes from its musical cooing call, said to sound like a person laughing; its other name comes from its habit of nesting among the fronds of palm trees. The bird's beautiful colouring has made it a favourite of bird-fanciers in many parts of the world since the 1860s, and escaped birds have established populations in various places – notably south-western Australia. Females are rather duller in colouring than males, whose eyes have a unique brown iris and red eye-ring. In hot areas they breed at any time of year, and may raise six or even eight broods a year.

Scientific name	*Streptopelia senegalensis*
Family	Columbidae
Size	25–27cm (10–10½in) long
Distribution	Much of Africa; Turkey; Middle East; southern Asia; feral elsewhere
Habitat	Mainly dry country – open woodland and scrub; gardens; fields; oases
Diet	Mainly seeds and grains; some insects
Breeding	Flimsy nest in tree, bush, at base of palm frond or on sheltered ledge of building; usually two eggs, incubated by both sexes for 12–14 days

Plumed or spinifex pigeon

The dry country of central and northern Australia, named after the spiky spinifex grass that is almost the only permanent vegetation, supports few resident bird species, but the plumed or spinifex pigeon is one. It has a lower metabolic rate than most birds, reducing its food and water needs, but it must have access to water at all times. For this reason, during periods of drought, flocks of the birds travel long distances if necessary to reach the few remaining waterholes. After the erratic rains fall, quick-growing plants spring up, flower and produce copious seed. The pigeons feed and drink freely – scurrying about the ground – and can breed and spread.

Scientific name	*Geophaps* (or *Lophophaps*) *plumifera*
Family	Columbidae
Size	20–23cm (8–9in) long
Distribution	Central and north-western Australia
Habitat	Semi-arid spinifex grasslands, espectially where hilly or mountainous
Diet	Mainly grass and other seeds; some insects and worms
Breeding	May breed at any time of year, depending on rains. Nest a scrape beside spinifex hummock; two eggs, incubated by both sexes for 16–18 days

Common or scaly-breasted ground dove

As their name suggests, ground doves spend their days mostly on the ground, searching for fallen seeds, berries and insects, nodding their head as they walk. The common or scaly-breasted ground dove (named after its feather pattern) may be confused with several doves with similar colouring in the Americas – notably the Inca dove (*Columbina inca*), which has a scaly pattern all over and lacks the ground dove's pinkish breast colouring, and the well-known and widespread mourning dove (*Zenaida macroura*), which has a scaly pattern only as a juvenile. These last two species are also larger than the ground dove, and have a longer tail.

Scientific name	*Columbina* (or *Columbigallina*) *passerina*
Family	Columbidae
Size	About 18cm (7in) long
Distribution	Southern North America to Ecuador and Brazil
Habitat	Open scrubland; cultivated land
Diet	Mainly seeds and berries; some insects
Breeding	Nest of sticks in low tree or bush; two eggs, incubated by both sexes for 12–14 days

Victoria crowned pigeon

New Guinea has more than 40 species of pigeon – most of them brightly coloured – that include the crowned pigeons, the largest members of the family. These reach the size of a small turkey (*see p.90*). They have 16 tail feathers rather than the 12 of other pigeons, but the most obvious feature is the superb fan-shaped, lacy crest of plumes on the head of both sexes. There are three species, with different-coloured plumage, in different parts of the island, but all live on the forest floor, flying heavily into the trees to roost and nest. The male shows off his crest and tail in his bowing courtship display; the female responds by displaying her wings.

Scientific name	*Goura victoria*
Family	Columbidae
Size	About 84cm (33in) long
Distribution	Northern New Guinea
Habitat	Highland rainforest
Diet	Seeds, fruits and berries; possibly insects
Breeding	Nest a large platform of sticks in tree; single egg, incubated by both sexes for about 30 days

Pheasant pigeon

Known also as the magnificent ground pigeon, both common names for this New Guinea species are apt, for it is a remarkably pheasant-like ground-living bird with beautifully coloured plumage. It is shy, and spends most of its days walking back and forth among the forest undergrowth, head extended, searching for food. It can fly only short distances, rising when disturbed or to roost in a tree with a loud clatter of its wings. The subspecies illustrated is the white-naped *Otidiphaps nobilis aruensis* of the Aru Islands, south-west of New Guinea. The more widespread principal subspecies, *O. n. nobilis*, has a green nape; another form has a grey collar.

Scientific name	*Otidiphaps nobilis*
Family	Columbidae
Size	About 45cm (18in) long
Distribution	New Guinea and adjacent islands
Habitat	Rainforest
Diet	Fruits; seeds; insects; snails
Breeding	Nest a platform of twigs low in tree or on ground between buttress roots; single egg, incubated by both parents for about 28 days

Large green pigeon

More than 20 species of green pigeons of the genus *Treron* live in tropical Asia and Africa. They are all yellowish-green, often with patches or shading of orange, yellow, mauve or other colours. They are all tree-dwellers that seldom visit the ground, and live on fruits, especially wild figs. They can open their bill wide to swallow these fruits whole, and have a hard muscular gizzard to digest them. (They pass the seeds undigested and in this way help to disperse them.) The large green pigeon lives in the forest canopy in lowland parts of south-east Asia. Much of this lowland forest is in danger of being destroyed by logging and clearance by farmers, endangering the pigeon, which lives only in virgin forest.

Scientific name	*Treron capellei*
Family	Columbidae
Size	About 36cm (14in) long
Distribution	Thailand; Peninsular Malaysia; Sumatra and adjacent islands; Borneo
Habitat	Lowland undeveloped forest
Diet	Fruits of wild fig trees (*Ficus* species), especially 'strangler' figs
Breeding	Nest a platform of twigs high in tree; one or two eggs; information on incubation not known

Rainbow lorikeet

In a brilliantly coloured family, the rainbow lorikeet is one of the gaudiest, fully justifying its name. The fact that these birds move around noisily screeching and chattering in flocks of up to 100 makes them both an impressive sight and impossible to miss. Not that they are difficult to find in the areas where they live, for they are not afraid of human contact and will often feed in gardens or even from people's hands. At night they roost in trees, flying to feeding areas at sunrise to gorge greedily on the nectar and pollen of one flowering tree before moving on to another. They show considerable regional colour variations; one form, for example, has a red rather than a yellow collar.

Scientific name	*Trichoglossus haematodus*
Family	Psittacidae
Size	25–28cm (10–11in) long
Distribution	Eastern Indonesia to Vanuatu; eastern and south-eastern Australia
Habitat	Forests and open woodland; coconut plantations; parks and gardens
Diet	Pollen and nectar of flowers; also blossoms, seeds, berries and insects
Breeding	Nests in cavity in hollow tree trunk or limb; two or sometimes three eggs, incubated by female for 23–25 days

Palm cockatoo

Cockatoos are among the most majestic of parrots, and the palm cockatoo is the largest of all cockatoos. It has a huge bill – as big as the rest of its head – with which it can prise open a nut whose shell a person would find difficult to crack with a stone. A favourite food is pandanus 'palm' (not a true palm) seeds – hence its common name. It roosts and feeds mainly in tall trees, but sometimes flies to the ground for fallen fruits. Several other species of black cockatoos live in Australia, but unlike the palm cockatoo have red, yellow or white bands on the tail. Another distinctive feature of the palm cockatoo is the bare pinkish to red flesh patches on its cheeks; their colour varies with the bird's stress level.

Scientific name	*Probosciger aterrimus*
Family	Psittacidae
Size	Up to 70cm (27½in) long
Distribution	New Guinea; north-eastern tip of Australia
Habitat	Tropical rainforest
Diet	Seeds; nuts; leaf-buds; berries and other friuits; some insect larvae
Breeding	Nests in tree hollow lined with chewed splinters of wood; single egg, incubated by female for 31–35 days

Kea

Well camouflaged by its olive-green plumage, the kea is hard to spot in its natural habitat, unless betrayed by its loud 'keea' call. But at the tourist and ski resorts of New Zealand's Southern Alps it amuses visitors with its antics as it scavenges for food. It is not so popular with sheep graziers. Ever since sheep were introduced to New Zealand in the 1830s and 40s, keas have been blamed for sheep deaths – even in mountainous areas where harsh weather is bound to kill some stock. Careful studies in the mid-20th century showed that, although the occasional 'rogue' kea does kill a sheep, the birds mostly attack only dead carcasses or severely weakened animals. Keas are now partially protected.

Scientific name	*Nestor notabilis*
Family	Psittacidae
Size	About 46cm (18in) long
Distribution	New Zealand – mainly South Island; also extreme south of North Island
Habitat	Forest up to 2000m (6500ft); feeds in scrub and grassland above treeline
Diet	Carrion; insects and grubs; vegetable matter; occasional live animals
Breeding	Polygynous. Nest in rock crevice or under boulder, lined with moss, twigs and leaves; two or three eggs, incubated by female for 23–24 days

Kakapo

Another green New Zealand parrot, the kakapo is unique in several ways. It is the heaviest, if not the longest, of all parrots, males weighing up to 3.4kg (7½lb). It is the only flightless parrot, living mainly on the ground but clambering into trees and bushes for food – then sometimes gliding down. It has owl-like facial discs, and is one of the few nocturnal parrots. But is also one of the rarest. It used to range over much of New Zealand, but predators such as rats, cats, dogs and stoats – introduced first by Polynesian settlers, then by Europeans – gradually killed the defenceless kakapos. Transferring survivors to small predator-free islands has saved the species for now, but only just over 60 birds survive.

Scientific name	*Strigops habroptilus*
Family	Psittacidae
Size	About 63cm (25in) long
Distribution	Survive on a few small New Zealand islands; probably extinct elsewhere
Habitat	Originally on steep, wooded and bushy slopes, and among rocks
Diet	Fruit, berries, nuts, seeds and other plant material; some insects
Breeding	Polygynous. Nest a cavity or a hollow dug in rock crevice or between
	tree roots; two or three eggs, incubated by female for about 30 days

Crimson rosella

With their rich crimson, black and blue plumage, crimson rosellas are beautiful but less common in eastern Australia than rainbow lorikeets (*see p.142*). However, they are often seen in gardens and orchards feeding on cultivated fruits in place of their basic diet of tree seeds. They fly in small groups, though immature birds that have recently left the nest form flocks of 50 or more. Two other rosellas, with their own common names, are now believed to be subspecies of the crimson rosella. They are the Adelaide rosella of South Australia: (*Platycercus elegans adelaidae*), which is orange-red, black and blue; and the yellow rosella of the Murray River (*P. e. flaveolus*), which is yellow, black and blue.

Scientific name	*Platycercus elegans*
Family	Psittacidae
Size	32–36cm (12½–14in) long
Distribution	Eastern and south-eastern Australia; introduced in New Zealand
Habitat	Coastal and mountainous rainforest and sclerophyl (eucalypt) forest
Diet	Seeds, especially of eucalypts and wattle (mimosa); fruit; insects
Breeding	Nest a hole in tree; four to eight eggs (usually five), incubated by female for about 21 days

Black-masked lovebird

The endearing habit of pairs perching close together on a branch, preening each other's plumage, gives these small parrots their name and makes them favourites among caged-bird fanciers. The black-masked species is one of the best known even though it is native only to a small area of the Tanzanian highlands. It is often called simply the masked lovebird or green masked lovebird (from the colour of its wing feathers) because a blue-winged form has also been found wild and bred in captivity. It is closely related to other lovebirds, especially species with a white eye-ring such as the orange and green Fischer's lovebird (*Agapornis fischeri*).

Scientific name	*Agapornis persona* (or *Agapornis personatus*)
Family	Psittacidae
Size	About 14cm (5½in) long
Distribution	Highlands of Tanzania; introduced in coastal Tanzania and Kenya
Habitat	Semi-arid grassland with scattered trees at 1000–1500m (3000–5000ft)
Diet	Mainly seeds; also berries, buds and leaves
Breeding	Pairs for life. Domed nest of twigs and bark in hole in tree or in building; four to six eggs, incubated by female for 18–23 days

Blue and yellow macaw

The macaws of Central and South America are the biggest parrots and the most colourful of all the large species. The blue and yellow macaw is a flamboyant bird of the forest canopy that advertises its presence both by its plumage and also with raucous shrieking calls. Seen from above, its colour makes a vivid contrast to the trees' foliage, as pairs (or flocks made up of pairs) fly from one roost or feeding site to another. Like cockatoos, macaws have a huge bill that easily cracks the shell of the hardest seeds and nuts. Several species – including the blue and yellow macaw and the scarlet macaw (*Ara macao*) – are often seen in zoos. The hyacinth macaw (*Anodorhynchus hyacinthinus*) is the biggest of all.

Scientific name	*Ara araucana*
Family	Psittacidae
Size	About 86cm (34in) long
Distribution	Central and South America from Panama to Paraguay
Habitat	Rainforests and palm groves near waterways
Diet	Fruits; seeds; nuts
Breeding	Details uncertain, but nests in hole high in tree; usually two eggs, incubated solely or mainly by female for about 24–28 days

Golden conure

The beautiful golden-yellow plumage of this medium-sized, slender parrot contrasts with the green flight feathers. It is native to a relatively small area of the Brazilian rainforest, and has become seriously endangered in recent decades due to destruction of the rainforest and its flooding by dams, shooting for sport and food, and its capture for sale as a cage-bird. It now has legal protection in Brazil, but is still in decline. Golden conures are sociable birds that fly in pairs or small flocks in the forest canopy, screeching loudly to each other. Male birds perform an elaborate courtship display and, although they do not share in incubating the eggs, they protect the nest and help to feed the chicks.

Scientific name	*Aratinga* (or *Guaruba*) *guarouba*
Family	Psittacidae
Size	33–36cm (13–14in) long
Distribution	North-eastern Brazil
Habitat	Upland dry rainforest, usually near waterways
Diet	Fruits; seeds; nuts
Breeding	Nests in cavity high in forest tree; usually three to five eggs, incubated by female for 25–30 days

Blue-fronted amazon

The stout-bodied, short-tailed amazon parrots are among the best mimics of the human voice, and are commonly kept as caged birds. They are mostly green in colour, with yellow and often also red and blue patches. The blue-fronted species (also known simply as the blue-fronted parrot) has a small patch of pale blue at the base of the bill, below the crown. It lives in more open forest than many South American parrots, feeding and nesting in the tree-tops and often forming large groups. They may raid farmland for food. The closely related yellow-headed amazon or yellow-headed parrot (*Amazona ochrocephala*) of Central America to northern Brazil is one of the best 'talking' species.

Scientific name	*Amazona aestiva*
Family	Psittacidae
Size	35–40cm (14–16in) long
Distribution	North-eastern Brazil and Bolivia to northern Argentina
Habitat	Forests; sometimes ventures onto farmland to feed
Diet	Fruits; seeds; nuts; buds; flowers
Breeding	Nests in hollow in large tree; usually two to four eggs, incubated by female for about 28 days

Budgerigar

No member of the parrot family is so thoroughly domesticated as the budgerigar. A native of inland Australia – where it sometimes occurs, if rains provide ample food, in vast flocks – millions of these small, friendly birds are kept as caged pets. They belong to the group known as parakeets. In the wild they are primarily green and yellow, but numerous colour varieties have been bred in captivity. Sadly, caged budgerigars are unable to fly in the fast, agile way that flocks do in the open, where they may travel long distances to find food and water. The name (sometimes spelt, especially in Australia, 'budgerygar') comes from their Australian aboriginal name.

Scientific name	*Melopsittacus undulatus*
Family	Psittacidae
Size	About 18cm (7in) long
Distribution	Australia (mainly interior; migrates with available food and water)
Habitat	Open scrub and grasslands
Diet	Almost entirely seeds of grasses and other small plants
Breeding	Breeds any time of year, usually after rains. Nests in hollow in tree, post or stump; usually four to six eggs, incubated by female for 18 days

Livingstone's turaco

Turacos are soft-feathered African birds that were for a long time thought to be relatives of the cuckoos. However, DNA evidence has recently suggested that they are more closely related to the owls, and they are now often placed in a major group, or order, of their own – the Musophagiformes. They are spectacularly coloured, with green and red pigments that are found in no other types of bird. Like most other species, Livingstone's turaco has a prominent head-crest and a brightly coloured stubby beak ideal for eating forest fruits. Turacos are agile climbers; the fourth toe on each foot can be turned either way to help when climbing a tree.

Scientific name	*Tauraco livingstonii*; sometimes classified as *Tauraco persa livingstonii*
Family	Musophagidae
Size	About 45cm (18in) long
Distribution	Eastern Africa from Tanzania and Burundi to Mozambique
Habitat	Humid forests
Diet	Mainly fruits; some insects and grubs
Breeding	Nest a platform of twigs in tree; usually two or three eggs, incubated by both sexes for 21–24 days

Red-winged crested cuckoo

Cuckoos are well known for two characteristics: their call, which is made clearly only by the common cuckoo (*Cuculus canorus*) of Europe, Africa and Asia, and which gives this bird and the whole family their name; and their parasitic habit of laying their eggs in other birds' nests, which extends over about 45 species. In the case of the red-winged crested cuckoo (known equally as the chestnut-winged cuckoo), the female chooses mainly the nests of babblers and laughing thrushes (*see p.253*). Unlike the common cuckoo, the young of this species do not seem to evict the foster parents' true offspring from the nest, but are raised as part of the brood.

Scientific name	*Clamator* (or *Cuculus*) *coromandus*
Family	Cuculidae
Size	About 45cm (18in) long
Distribution	India to south-western China, Indochina and Indonesia
Habitat	Woodland; open forest; scrubland
Diet	Mainly insects (including large caterpillars)
Breeding	Nest parasite; female lays eggs in nests of other birds (usually two, but up to four in each); incubated by foster parent for about 10–12 days

African emerald cuckoo

Several species of beautiful green parasitic cuckoos live in Africa. The emerald cuckoo has bright green back and wing feathers and golden-yellow underparts. The female chooses mainly the nests of bulbuls, orioles, shrikes and weaver birds – species that generally nest high up in trees – to lay her eggs. Closely related species include Klaas's cuckoo (*Chrysococcyx klass*), with green and bronze wings; and the didric (or diedrik) cuckoo (*C. caprius*), with bronze-green wing and back plumage and white underparts with black barring. The latter's name comes from the male's distinctive mating call, 'dee-dee-dee-drik'; it lives in open woodland and savannah.

Scientific name	*Chrysococcyx cuprius*
Family	Cuculidae
Size	18–20cm (7–8in) long
Distribution	Africa south of Sahara
Habitat	Forest edges and clearings
Diet	Insects and larvae, including caterpillars and beetles
Breeding	Nest parasite; female lays single egg in nest of each foster parent, which incubates egg for about 10–12 days and feeds chick

Koel

Male

Female

A migratory species (which, for example, flies from New Guinea and Indonesia south to Australia to breed in the southern summer), the koel is named after the repeated, shrieking 'ko-el' or 'coo-ee' call made mainly by the male. The sexes look quite different, but the young are black like the adult male – an advantage when the eggs are laid in the nest of a crow such as the house crow (*Corvus splendens*) of India, whose young look very similar. Female koels also commonly lay their eggs in the nests of honeyeaters such as friarbirds (*see p.267*) and of orioles (*p.296*). Adult koels eat mainly fruits, but the young accept whatever their foster parent offers.

Scientific name	*Eudynamys scolopacea*
Family	Cuculidae
Size	40–46cm (16–18in) long
Distribution	Pakistan and India to southern China, south-east Asia and Australia
Habitat	Forest edge; open woodland; scrubland; farmland; gardens
Diet	Mainly fruits (especially wild figs); also insects and snails
Breeding	Nest parasite; female lays single egg in nest of each foster parent,
	which incubates egg for 13–14 days and feeds chick

Sunda ground cuckoo

This highly endangered member of the cuckoo family is now believed by many experts to consist of two distinct but similar species, the Bornean ground cuckoo (*Carpococcyx radiceus*) and the Sumatran ground cuckoo (*C. viridis*), previously regarded as a subspecies of the Bornean form. Like other ground cuckoos, such as their relatives the malcohas (*Rhopodytes, Ramphococcyx* and other genera), these birds are not nest parasites. Ground-living birds that can fly only poorly, they build a nest on the ground and incubate their own eggs. Both Sumatran and Bornean forms are threatened by forest destruction, and are rare even in national parks.

Scientific name	*Carpococcyx radiceus*
Family	Cuculidae
Size	About 60cm (24in) long
Distribution	Borneo; Sumatra
Habitat	Lowland forest and scrub, up to 1400–1700m (4500–5500ft)
Diet	Ground-living insects and other small creatures
Breeding	Not parasitic. Builds nest of leaves and sticks on ground; other details uncertain

Black-faced coucal

Coucals are mainly ground-living relatives of the true ground cuckoos. They are found in most of sub-Saharan Africa and in southern and south-east Asia and Australia, extending to some islands of the south-western Pacific. They have strong legs, and generally run rather than fly from danger; they fly slowly and poorly on their short, rounded wings. They are not nest parasites, but build domed nests usually of grass. The black-faced coucal is one of several species endemic to various habitats in the Philippines; others include the Philippine coucal (*Centropus viridis*) of grassland and thickets, and the rufous coucal (*C. unirufus*) of bamboo forests.

Scientific name	*Centropus melanops*
Family	Cuculidae; often classified in separate family, Centropodidae
Size	About 45cm (18in) long
Distribution	Philippines
Habitat	Forests; forest edge
Diet	Insects and other small ground-living creatures
Breeding	Not parasitic. Builds large domed nest of grass near ground, with side entrance; three to five eggs, incubated by both sexes for about 14 days

Greater roadrunner

Perhaps best known as a cartoon character, the roadrunner is famous for its ability to run quickly – head and long tail extended – on its long legs. Speeds of up to 37km/h (23mph) have been measured, but roadrunners are poor fliers and prefer to run from enemies as well as when chasing prey. Natives of the desert country of the American south-west, they are sometimes known as chaparral cocks. They are not afraid of attacking dangerous adversaries – even small rattlesnakes – usually killing with a sudden pounce. Roadrunners are partially cold-blooded, allowing their body temperature to fall on cold nights in order to conserve energy.

Scientific name	*Geococcyx californianus*
Family	Cuculidae; often classified separately in Coccyzidae or Neomorphidae
Size	50–60cm (20–24in) long
Distribution	South-western United States to central Mexico
Habitat	Deserts and semi-deserts
Diet	Lizards and small snakes; insects; scorpions; fruits of prickly-pear cactus
Breeding	Pairs and holds territory for life. Not parasitic. Nest a shallow cup in bush, tree or cactus stump; two to six eggs, incubated for about 20 days

Common or smooth-billed ani

The huge bill, large head and stout body make this species look quite unlike any other members of the cuckoo group. It has a long, wedge-shaped tail and rather weak wings, with which it flies poorly. It spends most of the time on the ground in small groups, searching for insects and often following grazing cattle for the creatures their hooves disturb. However, the most remarkable feature of all three species of ani is their habit of communal nesting and breeding. Some pairs build their own nest, but generally a whole group builds one large nest, in which several females lay their eggs – up to 25 in all – then share incubation and feeding duties.

Scientific name	*Crotophaga ani*
Family	Cuculidae; often classified separately in Coccyzidae or Crotophagidae
Size	30–36cm (12–14in) long
Distribution	Southern Florida and Caribbean to Argentina; Galápagos Islands
Habitat	Forest edge; grassland; grazing land
Diet	Mostly ground-living insects such as grasshoppers; fruit; berries
Breeding	Not parasitic. Twiggy nest in tree or bush for one or several pairs; each female lays three or four eggs and shares incubation for about 14 days

Common barn owl

Owls account for more than half of all nocturnal bird species, and they are well adapted for hunting at night. They have large, forward-facing eyes, acute hearing, and sharp, hooked claws for catching and killing their prey. Their eyes are surrounded by characteristic disks of feathers, which in barn owls form a heart shape. These owls have probably lived near human settlements for thousands of years, and their eerie shrieking call and ghostly appearance when flying overhead at night have no doubt given rise to many legends of haunted ruins. There are more than 30 subspecies worldwide, some with brownish rather than white underparts.

Scientific name	*Tyto alba*
Family	Tytonidae
Size	33–36cm (13–14in) long
Distribution	Almost worldwide except poles, northern Asia, extreme North America
Habitat	Almost all types of open country with trees, often near buildings
Diet	Rats, mice and other small animals; small birds
Breeding	Pairs for life. Nests in hole in tree, rock crevice or often in barn or other
	building; four to seven eggs, incubated by female for about 33 days

Spectacled owl

The unique white-on-black facial pattern gives the spectacled owl its name, but this is even more apt for juvenile birds, which are all-white except for two black 'spectacles'. It is a species mainly of dense jungle, particularly near water, but is also found in plantations and other wooded habitats. Spectacled owls are mostly nocturnal – hunting especially on moonlit nights – but are also sometimes active during the day. They have excellent sight, and perch on a branch until they spot suitable prey, then swoop. They have a long call like a series of taps, but the female also makes a hawk-like screech. The young leave the nest well before they can fly, but often remain with their parents for up to a year.

Scientific name	*Pulsatrix perspicillata*
Family	Strigidae
Size	About 45cm (18in) long
Distribution	Southern Mexico to northern Argentina, east of Andes
Habitat	Forests, including rainforests, open woodland and mangroves
Diet	Insects; tree frogs; lizards; bats; birds; crabs; insects
Breeding	Nests in large hole in tree; up to three (but usually one or two) eggs, incubated for about 35–36 days

Tengmalm's owl

Asmall but large-headed owl, Tengmalm's owl has close-set eyes and prominent facial disks, with raised eyebrows, that together give it a look of surprise. It is an almost entirely nocturnal species, largely of dense coniferous forest – both natural and planted – although it sometimes appears in clearings or in the more open plantings of the forest fringe. It hides among tree foliage by day, so is difficult to see. It is more likely to be heard, males making a series of hooting sounds – 'poh-poh-poh-poh-poh' – that vary slightly in pitch and length between individuals. There are at least seven geographical subspecies, some of them migrating south in winter.

Scientific name	*Aegolius funereus*
Family	Strigidae
Size	24–27cm (9½–10½in) long
Distribution	Northern Eurasia; northern and south-western North America
Habitat	Mainly coniferous forests; some mixed and upland birch forests
Diet	Small rodents (voles; mice; shrews); small birds
Breeding	Nests in hole in tree (often large woodpecker hole); usually three to six eggs, incubated by female for about 29 days

Verreaux's eagle owl

Eagle owls and horned owls of the genus *Bubo* are the world's largest owls, marked by their prominent ear tufts. The biggest species of all is the Eurasian eagle owl (*B. bubo*), which lives from the Atlantic to the Pacific and as far south as the Sahara. Verreaux's eagle owl (also known as the giant or milky eagle owl) of the parts of Africa farther to the south is very little smaller, and is a formidable hunter. It will catch prey up to its own size, such as helmeted guineafowl (*see p.95*), or items as small as moths. It will wade in water to catch fish or will scavenge on carrion. Verreaux's eagle owl hunts mainly in the evening, and has been observed standing up to an aggressive eagle challenging it for its catch.

Scientific name	*Bubo lacteus*
Family	Strigidae
Size	60–66cm (24–26in) long
Distribution	Most of sub-Saharan Africa, except Congo basin
Habitat	Forests, open woodland and savannah with scattered trees
Diet	Mammals (including monkeys and hedgehogs); birds; other creatures
Breeding	Uses old stick nests of vultures, crows or other birds; usually two eggs, incubated by female for about 35 days

Eurasian pygmy owl

Pygmy owls are among the smallest owls, and the Eurasian species has a small head, chubby body and proportionately long tail. The facial mask is less definite than in most other owls, but it has short white 'eyebrows'. It is an elusive bird, best seen hunting at dusk and dawn; in winter it is more likely to venture onto cultivated land and around farmyards. It chases and catches small birds on the wing – even species such as thrushes that are almost its own size. Like all owls, it eats small prey whole, later expelling a pellet containing the undigestible bones, fur and other parts. Closely related species of pygmy owls live in Africa and the Americas.

Scientific name	*Glaucidium passerinum*
Family	Strigidae
Size	15–19cm (6–7½in) long; female slightly larger than male
Distribution	Northern and central Europe east to eastern Siberia and northern China
Habitat	Mainly coniferous and upland mixed forest, especially with clearings
Diet	Small birds, mammals (especially rodents), lizards and other creatures
Breeding	Nests in hole in tree (usually woodpecker hole); three to seven eggs, incubated by female for 28–29 days

Burrowing owl

A small, mainly ground-living owl with a short tail and a permanent 'frown', the burrowing owl has a slightly comical appearance. It takes refuge and breeds underground – sometimes in a burrow it digs for itself but more often an abandoned burrow taken over from a prairie dog, viscacha, gopher, armadillo or other animal. Burrowing owls hunt mainly at dawn and dusk, but males may be seen during the day standing guard on a mound or fence post near the burrow. They hunt from the air and on the ground, often following horses to catch small creatures they disturb. Several subspecies live in various areas of the large range.

Scientific name	*Athene* (or *Speotyto*) *cunicularia*
Family	Strigidae
Size	18–25cm (7–10in) long
Distribution	Southern Canada to southern South America, except Andes and jungle
Habitat	Open grassy plains; pasture; desert and semi-desert; mountain slopes
Diet	Insects such as beetles and grasshoppers; small mammals; birds; fruits
Breeding	Nests in burrow (dug by self or abandoned by other animal); up to 11
	(usually five or six) eggs, incubated for about 28 days

Oilbird

Oilbirds are remarkable in many ways. They are highly sociable, nesting in colonies of up to 50 pairs in deep caves. They are entirely nocturnal, roosting all day and emerging at night to feed on tree (especially palm) fruits, and are the only nocturnal fruit-eating birds. They have large eyes, but these are useless in the gloom of a cave, and they find their way by echo-location, like bats; they make a clicking noise (audible to humans) and locate obstacles by the echo. They feed on the wing, swallowing the fruits whole and later regurgitating the seeds. They feed the oil-rich fruits to their nestlings – which grow to weigh half as much again as one of their parents. Local people catch and boil them for their oil.

Scientific name	*Steatornis caripensis*
Family	Steatornithidae
Size	About 45cm (18in) long
Distribution	Peru to Panama, Venezuela and French Guiana; Trinidad
Habitat	Mountainous and coastal areas
Diet	Oily tree fruits, especially of palms
Breeding	Nests in colonies in caves. Nest a mound of regurgitated seeds on ledge; two to four eggs, incubated by both sexes for about 33 days

Australian owlet nightjar

Sometimes known as the owlet frogmouth or moth owl, this bird is common throughout Australia but is secretive and seldom seen. By day it roosts in a hole, coming out to feed at night – though it may be seen warming itself at the entrance to the hole on sunny winter days. It is a small bird, with soft plumage, big brown eyes and a small hooked bill (but large gape) surrounded by bristles. It has a rather owl-like flat face, but also resembles both nightjars and frogmouths, its true relatives. It is believed to feed both on the wing – catching insects in flight in its large mouth – and on the ground, where it picks up ants, millipedes and similar creatures.

Scientific name	*Aegotheles cristatus*
Family	Aegothelidae
Size	About 22cm (8½in) long
Distribution	Throughout Australia (including Tasmania); southern New Guinea
Habitat	All types of country, especially arid interior; rare in wet forest
Diet	Insects and other invertebrates
Breeding	Nests in hole in tree, bank or cliff, lined with leaves; three to five eggs; incubation period uncertain

Tawny frogmouth

The name frogmouth aptly describes the huge, gaping mouth of this bird, with its triangular hooked bill. It is one of about 14 species of frogmouths, of which 11 Asian native species are sometimes classified in a separate family, the Batrachostomidae. The tawny frogmouth is a tree-dweller that spends its day motionless on a branch, so well camouflaged by its colouring and its lengthwise perch that it looks like a dead branch and can hardly be seen. It becomes active at dusk, watching for ground-living prey from its perch and then flying down on its weak, rounded wings to pounce on it. Tawny frogmouths vary considerably in size and colour across Australia, and probably comprise several subspecies.

Scientific name	*Podargus strigoides*
Family	Podargidae
Size	34–45cm (13½–18in) long
Distribution	Most of Australia except most arid parts of interior
Habitat	Anywhere there are trees, but especially eucalypt woodland
Diet	Mainly ground-living insects and other invertebrates
Breeding	Nest a frail platform of sticks and leaves on branch or fork of tree; two or three eggs, incubated by female for about 30 days

Common or grey potoo

Potoos get their name from their plaintive night-time call. They roost bolt-upright on a stump or tree branch during the day, camouflaged by their colouring and posture in much the same way as their Australian cousins the frogmouths. They have a small, hooked bill but a wide gape, which they use to catch insects on the wing, darting out from their perch whenever they spot a suitable morsel. Unlike other members of the group, they have no bristles around the bill. Experts have recently suggested that the northern potoo of Central America and the Caribbean should be split off as a separate species, *Nyctibius jamaicensis*, from the main species, *N. griseus*. Both birds are very similar.

Scientific name	*Nyctibius griseus* and *N. jamaicensis* (*see above*)
Family	Nictibiidae
Size	About 40cm (16in) long
Distribution	Tropical Central and South America; parts of Caribbean
Habitat	Open forest and forest edge; farmland with trees
Diet	Mainly insects
Breeding	Lays single egg in small hollow in top of tree stump, or in knot-hole in branch; incubated by both sexes (period uncertain)

Eurasian nightjar

The genus name *Caprimulgus* means 'goat-sucker' – a reference to an ancient myth that these birds suck the milk of goats. Nightjars are nocturnal birds that actually eat moths and other evening- and night-flying insects, which they spot with their large eyes and catch on the wing with their wide-open, bristle-fringed mouth. They roost by day, flying only a short distance if disturbed. Their colouring camouflages them well, and they are seldom seen, but in flight at dusk they resemble a small hawk, turning and darting silently to and fro. They are more likely to be heard than seen: the purring or churring night-time call of the male during the breeding season is the origin of the name nightjar.

Scientific name	*Caprimulgus europaeus*
Family	Caprimulgidae
Size	26–28cm (10¼–11in) long
Distribution	Europe; North Africa; western and central Asia; migrates to South Africa
Habitat	Open wooded areas, clearings, heathland and semi-desert
Diet	Moths and other nocturnal insects
Breeding	Nest a shallow scrape or hollow in ground, usually near tree or bush; two eggs, incubated by both sexes for about 18 days

Standard-winged nightjar

Night-flying birds need special methods of attracting mates that can be seen in the evening gloom. These often involve aerial courtship displays, and the males of several nightjar species have evolved extreme methods of making themselves noticed. In the male standard-winged nightjar, one feather on each wing grows to an enormous length – up to 45cm (18in) – in the breeding season, with a flag-like tuft or vane at the end. They break off after breeding, the stubs are later moulted, and they then grow again the next season. The male pennant-winged nightjar (*Macrodipteryx* [or *Semeiophorus*] *vexillarius*) has long, streaming wing feathers without tufts.

Scientific name	*Macrodipteryx longipennis*
Family	Caprimulgidae
Size	Body 23–30cm (9–12in) long (*see above*)
Distribution	Sub-Saharan Africa (Senegal to Ethiopia); parts of Uganda and Kenya
Habitat	Open wooded savannah and scrub
Diet	Flying insects
Breeding	May be polygynous. Nest a hollow in ground, in clusters; two eggs, incubated by female, probably for about 18 days

Alpine swift

Swifts are the fastest and most completely aerial of all birds, thanks to their superbly streamlined shape. They have been tracked travelling more than 1600km (1000 miles) in three days, and timed flying at more than 160km/h (100mph). They feed, drink, bathe, sleep and even mate in the air. Some hardly ever come to land, although the alpine swift is one species that does sometimes roost at its nesting site. It is easily distinguished from the all-black common swift of Europe, Asia and Africa (*Apus apus*) by its white underparts and chin, with a black breast-band. Like other swifts, it catches small insects in its wide gape as it flies. It feeds its young on small 'parcels' of insects glued together with saliva.

Scientific name	*Tachymarptis* (or *Apus*) *melba*
Family	Apodidae
Size	20–22cm (8–8½in) long
Distribution	Southern Europe and Asia to Bangladesh; much of Africa
Habitat	Craggy uplands; cliffs; tall buildings
Diet	Small flying insects
Breeding	Cup-shaped nest of plant materials and feathers glued with saliva, in rock crevice or building; usually three eggs, incubated by both sexes

Grey-rumped tree-swift

Known also as the crested swift or crested tree-swift (a name shared with a related species, *Hemiprocne coronata*), this bird is one of a family of Asian tree-swifts that are less exclusively airborne than true swifts. It often perches on a tree-branch or cable, ready to swoop down to chase and catch any passing insects. It is also notable for its tiny nest, about 3cm (just over an inch) across and made from fragments of papery bark and feathers, glued together (and to a thin branch) with the birds' saliva. The parents perch on the branch itself to cover the egg and incubate it. (Even more precariously, palm swifts of the genus *Cypsiurus* simply glue their egg to a palm frond, to which they then cling to incubate the egg.)

Scientific name	*Hemiprocne longipennis*
Family	Hemiprocnidae
Size	20–23cm (8–9in) long
Distribution	Malaysia and Indonesia as far east as Sulawesi (Celebes)
Habitat	Lowland forest edges; open woodland; farmland; towns
Diet	Small flying insects
Breeding	Tiny fragile nest of bark flakes glued with saliva on tree branch; single bluish egg, incubated by both parents

173

Sword-billed hummingbird

Hummingbirds are the jewels of the bird world – mostly tiny, with iridescent plumage and wings that beat too fast to see, generating their humming sound. They all have a long bill – though none longer than that of the sword-billed species, which has the longest bill of any bird in relation to its size – and a tube-tipped tongue with which they sip nectar from deep down in forest flowers, while hovering in mid-air. (They fly so well that they can move in any direction, even backwards.) The sweet nectar gives them the energy they need to maintain the highest metabolic rate of all birds, while insects in the nectar provide protein. The sword-bill feeds from long, trumpet-shaped passionflowers.

Scientific name	*Ensifera ensifera*
Family	Trochilidae
Size	20–25cm (8–10in) long, including bill; body about 8cm (3in)
Distribution	Andes, from Venezuela to Bolivia
Habitat	Bushy slopes and forest edge at 1700–3300m (5600–10 800ft)
Diet	Nectar; insects
Breeding	Small cup-shaped nest of moss on branch, built by female; two eggs, incubated by female for about 16 days

Spatule-tail, or sylphide

Some hummingbirds are extremely rare and restricted to only small areas. The spatule-tail (also known as Lodigge's spatule-tail or racket-tail, or the marvellous spatule-tail) is one of these, living only in an isolated valley in the Peruvian Andes. For decades, it was known only by a single dead specimen of unknown origin. Then, in the late 19th century, its home was discovered – yet many of its habits are still little known. The male has an extremely long tail with only four feathers, two of which are flexible and wire-like, ending in rounded 'spatules'. The bird uses these feathers to frame his iridescent head and throat plumage during courtship.

Scientific name	*Loddigesia mirabilis*
Family	Trochilidae
Size	About 25cm (10in), including male's tail feathers; female 12cm (5in)
Distribution	Andes of Peru
Habitat	Single wooded valley at 2450–2750m (8000–9000ft)
Diet	Presumably nectar and insects
Breeding	Details uncertain, but probably small cup-shaped nest; probably two eggs, incubated by female for 14–19 days

White-tipped sicklebill

Some of the more than 300 species of hummingbirds have evolved in such close association with certain forest plants that they can feed only on the flowers of that plant or ones of similar shape. An example is the white-tipped sicklebill and its close relative the buff-tailed sicklebill (*Eutoxeres condamini*). Their bill is strongly curved downwards. As a result, it can feed on the nectar of heliconias and certain orchids, which cannot be reached by other hummingbirds; the disadvantage is that they cannot feed from other flowers. The curved bill makes it awkward to feed while hovering, as most hummingbirds do, so the birds often perch rather clumsily on their short legs on the flower as they suck its nectar.

Scientific name	*Eutoxeres aquila*
Family	Trochilidae
Size	About 12.5cm (5in) long
Distribution	Costa Rica to northern Peru, west of Andes
Habitat	Lowland humid forest undergrowth and thickets, to 2100m (6900ft)
Diet	Nectar; insects
Breeding	Long cup-shaped nest of plant fibres and spiders' webs, built by female; usually two eggs, incubated by female for about 16 days

Streamertail

Fewer than 20 hummingbird species are commonly seen in the West Indies, but the male streamertail of Jamaica (known locally as the long-tailed doctor bird) is the most spectacular of those. It has long, wavy outer tail feathers, which add to the whirring sound of the bird's flight and are used in courtship. Even after moulting the tail feathers, the male is easily recognized by the brilliant green plumage and black crown; the female is also green but has mainly white underparts. Most streamertails have a red bill (which is darker in females), but a black-billed form is found at the eastern end of the island. Some ornithologists believe that this is a separate species, *Trochilus scitulus*.

Scientific name	*Trochilus polytmus*
Family	Trochilidae
Size	About 25cm (10in) long, including male's tail; female about 11cm (4½in)
Distribution	Jamaica
Habitat	Open woodland and scrub, at all altitudes
Diet	Nectar; insects
Breeding	Small cup-shaped nest of plant fibres on branch of bush, built by female; generally two eggs, incubated by female for about 16 days

Anna's hummingbird

Most hummingbird species live in tropical Central and South America, but Anna's has been spotted as far north as southern Alaska and as far east as New Mexico and even Florida. It used to have a much more restricted range, but the planting of exotic flowering plants such as eucalypts and red-hot pokers, and people putting hummingbird-feeders in their gardens, have encouraged its spread. This has also been aided by its migratory habit. Its natural breeding ground is the chaparral of coastal California, where it nests in winter and early spring; it then escapes the summer heat by moving to higher country and feeding on alpine meadow flowers.

Scientific name	*Calypte anna*
Family	Trochilidae
Size	About 9.5cm (3¾in) long
Distribution	Western North America, from British Columbia to Mexico and Arizona
Habitat	Open woodland; chaparral; scrub; meadows; gardens
Diet	Nectar; insects
Breeding	Small cup-shaped nest of plant fibres bound with spiders' webs, built by female; two eggs, incubated by female for 16–17 days

Andean hillstar

The Andean hillstar's iridescent head plumage changes apparent colour with the angle of view. It is a native of much more rugged country than most hummingbirds, living in the harsh environment of the high Andes. It reduces its body temperature by night, becoming torpid (inactive) in order to conserve energy, and may take shelter by roosting in a cave. When feeding in exposed, windy places, it clings to a branch with its strong feet rather than hovering. The female is unusual for a hummingbird in being territorial, but as with most hummingbirds the male plays no part in building the nest, incubating the eggs, or caring for the young.

Scientific name	*Oreotrochilus estella*
Family	Trochilidae
Size	About 12.5cm (5in) long
Distribution	Andes, from Ecuador to northern Chile and north-western Argentina
Habitat	Rocky slopes up to 4600m (15 000ft)
Diet	Nectar; insects and small spiders
Breeding	Relatively large, well-insulated cup-shaped nest, on cliff face, cave entrance or building; usually two eggs, incubated by female for 16 days

Blue-naped mousebird or coly

Aslender, tapering tail, a plump body covered with soft grey, hair-like plumage, and a habit of scurrying among foliage as they forage – all make mousebirds' name very apt. They belong to an ancient group of birds, native only to Africa, that have no close relatives. There are six species, living in overlapping territories through most of Africa south of the Sahara. They are gregarious birds, living in flocks of up to 30 and huddling close together when they roost at night. Their outer two toes are reversible at will: they can grasp a perch with all four toes pointing forward, with three forward and one back, or with two forward and two back. They perch with feet wide apart, often grasping two separate stems.

Scientific name	*Urocolius* (or *Colius*) *macrourus*
Family	Coliidea
Size	About 35cm (14in) long, including tail
Distribution	Band of sub-Saharan Africa, as far south as south-western Tanzania
Habitat	Semi-arid woodland; thorn scrub
Diet	Mainly green leaves
Breeding	Nest an untidy shallow cup made of plant material, lined with leaves; usually two to four eggs, incubated by both sexes for 12–14 days

Quetzal

Nominated by many bird-lovers as the world's most beautiful bird, the quetzal – specifically the resplendent quetzal, to distinguish it from four other species – is the national bird of Guatemala. Centuries ago, the Aztec and Maya people of Central America revered the bird and used the male's long tail plumes for ceremonial decoration. It was part of their 'plumed serpent' god Quetzalcoatl. The plumes grow from the tail coverts – the feathers that grow over the tail proper – and are displayed in courtship and in territory-marking flights. The male shares in incubation duties, entering the nesting hole head-first, then turning round so that the plumes lie over his head and project from the entrance.

Scientific name	*Pharomachrus mocinno*
Family	Trogonidae
Size	About 36cm (14in) long, excluding male's tail – adds about 60cm (24in)
Distribution	Americas from southern Mexico to Panama
Habitat	Rainforest and open woodland at 1200–3500m (4000–11 500ft)
Diet	Fruits; insects; frogs and other small animals
Breeding	Nest a hole in tree; usually two or three eggs, incubated by both sexes for 17–19 days

White-tailed trogon

The colourful trogons are forest-living birds of the Americas, Africa and southern and south-eastern Asia. The American species, such as the white-tailed trogon, have notches or serrations in the sides of their bill that help in snatching small fruits from jungle trees. They do this in flight, then perch on a branch to eat. They catch insects in a similar manner, dashing out from a perch to catch their prey as it flies past or crawls on a nearby leaf. Trogons' legs are small and weak, and the inner (first and second) toes point backwards while the outer ones point to the front – an aid to grasping branches. In other birds with a similar arrangement, it is the first and fourth toes that point back.

Scientific name	*Trogon viridis*
Family	Trogonidae
Size	About 24cm (9½in) long
Distribution	Central and South America, from Panama to south-eastern Brazil
Habitat	Rainforest and open woodland, to 1300m (4300ft)
Diet	Fruits; insects
Breeding	Nest a deep hole in tree; two to four roundish eggs, incubated by both sexes for 17–19 days

Cuban trogon

Despite their proximity to the trogons' major territory in Central America, the islands of the Caribbean have only two species of these colourful birds. Each is native to one of the larger islands, Cuba and Hispaniola. The Cuban trogon and the Hispaniolan species (*Temnotrogon roseigaster*) are rather similar, with mostly green upper parts (plus a violet-blue crown in the Cuban trogon), and they are now often grouped in the same genus, *Priotelus*. The Cuban trogon is known locally as the tocoloro or tocororo, after its repetitive call. The tip of its tail is rather ragged, unlike that of most trogons, which is generally squared. It is rather inactive and, like all trogons, rarely leaves its territory.

Scientific name	*Priotelus temnurus*
Family	Trogonidae
Size	25–28cm (10–11in) long
Distribution	Cuba and its offshore island, Isle of Pines
Habitat	Forests, mainly in mountains
Diet	Small fruits; insects
Breeding	Nests in hollow tree or stump; two to four eggs, incubated by both sexes for about 17–19 days

Narina trogon

The three African members of the trogon family are more predominantly insect-eaters than their American cousins. The narina trogon is the most widespread species. It inhabits both dense forest and more open woodland, perching motionless for minutes on a branch or creeper, watching for suitable food morsels. It sometimes creeps along the branch to catch its prey, but more often plucks an insect or caterpillar from a leaf or twig while hovering in the air. It may also catch prey in mid-air, and eats a few berries. Although the sexes differ, the female narina trogon is almost as colourful as the male; its chest is brown rather than green. The male makes a soft coo-ing call rather like a dove.

Scientific name	*Apaloderma narina*
Family	Trogonidae
Size	About 30cm (12in) long
Distribution	Much of sub-Saharan Africa
Habitat	Forests and woodland
Diet	Mainly insects; some berries and small fruits
Breeding	Nests in hollow tree or stump; usually two or three eggs, incubated by both sexes for about 20 days

Red-naped trogon

The 11 trogon species of Asia show much more marked sexual dimorphism (differences between males and females) than those of Africa and the Americas. In general, their plumage is brilliantly coloured red, orange and brown in males, but females are a much duller brown with lighter markings. The male red-naped species has a flash of red behind the eyes. Like other trogon species, it perches on a branch for long periods, dashing off to snatch prey – large insects or other small animals – from a branch or leaf. All trogons have a number of unique anatomical features, including a single carotid artery in the neck and extremely thin skin, to which the soft feathers are rather loosely attached.

Scientific name	*Harpactes kasumba*
Family	Trogonidae
Size	About 30cm (12in) long
Distribution	Malaysia; Sumatra; Borneo
Habitat	Lowland forests up to 500m (1600ft)
Diet	Mainly large insects; also small frogs and lizards
Breeding	Nest a hollow in tree; usually two or three eggs, incubated by both sexes for about 17–19 days

White-throated kingfisher

Brilliantly coloured turquoise-blue and rusty-red – rather like the common kingfisher (*Alcedo atthis*) of Europe and Asia, but twice the length – the white-throated (or white-breasted) kingfisher has a thicker, bright red bill. This relates to its diet, which consists mostly of land creatures, unlike the fish eaten by the common kingfisher. Both swoop on their prey to catch it in their bill, the common kingfisher diving headlong into water for fish. The white-throated species carries its prey back to a perch – usually a branch – and pounds it against the perch to soften it before bolting it down. Kingfishers are poor walkers, but hop stiffly on the ground.

Scientific name	*Halcyon smyrnensis*
Family	Alcedinidae; may be classified separately in Halcyonidae or Dacelonidae
Size	About 28cm (11in) long
Distribution	Southern Asia, from Turkey to China, Taiwan and Philippines
Habitat	Open country; fields; woods; towns; some lakes and coasts
Diet	Insects; crabs; frogs; small reptiles and other animals; fish
Breeding	Nests in chamber at end of tunnel dug in earth bank; four to seven eggs, incubated by both sexes for 16–20 days

Laughing kookaburra

The largest of all kingfishers, the kookaburra makes a loud, cackling call in a characteristic posture on its perch, with its head and tail raised. The purpose of the call is to claim and advertise the bird's territory, and one bird will often be joined by other nearby birds, generating a whole chorus of manic 'laughter'. Young kookaburras stay in their parents' territory for several years as 'nest helpers'; they help to protect the territory, collect food for nestlings and even take turns incubating the eggs. Kookaburras' diet – including insects, rodents and snakes – makes them welcome to farmers. They seize snakes, even highly venomous ones, behind the head, and kill them by dropping or battering them.

Scientific name	*Dacelo novaeguineae* (or, incorrectly, *D. gigas*)
Family	Alcedinidae; may be classified separately in Halcyonidae or Dacelonidae
Size	About 45cm (18in) long
Distribution	Eastern, south-eastern and south-western Australia; not New Guinea
Habitat	Woodland and open forest
Diet	Insects and other invertebrates; snakes and lizards; rodents; small birds
Breeding	Nests in any large cavity, usually in tree or termite mound; up to four (usually two) eggs, incubated by both sexes and 'helpers' for 23–24 days

Broad-billed tody

Five species of the tiny, colourful todies make up the only bird family restricted entirely to the West Indies. They are very closely related, all belonging to the genus *Todus* and all predominantly bright green, red and white. They all feed by watching for insects from a perch and then darting out with whirring wings to catch their prey in mid-air. They nest in a burrow dug in the earth, usually of a bank. One species each live in Cuba, Jamaica and Puerto Rico, and two in Hispaniola – where they are called *barrancolí* (bank-dwellers). The narrow-billed Hispaniolan tody (*Todus angustirostris*) is a highland species, the broad-billed a lowland species.

Scientific name	*Todus subulatus*
Family	Todidae
Size	About 11.5cm (4½in) long
Distribution	Hispaniola (Haiti and Dominican Republic) and adjacent Gonâve island
Habitat	Lowland open and semi-arid country
Diet	Mainly insects; sometimes very small lizards
Breeding	Nests in chamber at end of short, narrow burrow in earth bank; usually three or four eggs, incubated by both sexes

Blue-crowned motmot

A distinctive feature of six out of the nine motmot species – including the blue-crowned – is the long, dangling central tail feathers. These feathers lose their barbs (the branches that form the feathers' vane, or blade) from the part just above the end. The barbs are loosely attached, and work loose with preening and through brushing against vegetation. As a result, they leave a racket-like or spoon-shaped tip to the tail. Like the closely related todies and many kingfishers, motmots watch for prey from a perch, dart out to catch it, then return to the perch to eat it. A number of distinctive subspecies live in various parts of the bird's range, some of which – especially in the high Andes – are probably separate species.

Scientific name	*Momotus momota*
Family	Momotidae
Size	About 40cm (16in) long
Distribution	Americas from Mexico to north-western Argentina
Habitat	Forests and clearings; plantations; gardens
Diet	Insects; spiders; small lizards; fruit (especially bananas)
Breeding	Nests in chamber at end of long burrow dug in wet season in soft bank; three or four eggs, laid in dry season and incubated by both sexes

Carmine bee-eater

Huge flocks of these brilliantly coloured birds live on the African plains. They hunt insects from a perch or in long, gliding flights interspersed with sudden dashes. They kill many honey-bees (often dashing them to death and squeezing out the venom before swallowing them), but also eat vast numbers of swarming locusts. They sometimes hunt from the back of an ostrich or a bustard (*see pp.14 & 107*), which stirs up ground-living insects. The northern species illustrated has a southern African counterpart with a pink rather than blue chin. Some ornithologists classify it as a separate species, *Merops nubicoides*, others as a subspecies of *M. nubicus*.

Scientific name	*Merops nubicus*
Family	Meropidae
Size	33–38cm (13–15in) long
Distribution	Central Africa, from Senegal and Somalia to Tanzania (*see above*)
Habitat	Open woodland; savannah and other grassland
Diet	Bees and wasps; ants; termites; locusts; other insects
Breeding	Nests in large colonies, each pair in chamber at end of burrow in earth; two to four eggs, incubated by both sexes for about 21 days

Lilac-breasted roller

Rollers get their name from the males' spectacular tumbling aerobatic displays during courtship. They differ from other birds in the group in having the two inner toes on each foot joined together for much of their length. The lilac-breasted species is one of the best known African members of this colourful family, easily recognized by its colouring and its sharply forked tail. It tends to hunt from a perch, dashing out to catch flying insects or swooping down to the ground for a tasty grasshopper or lizard. It eats large quantities of swarming ants and locusts, and is among the first birds to feed on fleeing creatures driven into the open by a fire. The southernmost populations migrate northwards for food in winter.

Scientific name	*Coracias caudata*
Family	Coraciidae
Size	About 40cm (16in) long
Distribution	Eastern and central Africa, from Ethiopia to Angola and South Africa
Habitat	Woodland; savannah; farmland; gardens
Diet	Insects; spiders; some small lizards and birds
Breeding	Nests in cavity in dead tree or termite mound; usually two or three eggs, incubated by both sexes for 18–20 days

Dollar bird, or broad-billed roller

The name dollar bird comes from the round, pale blue patches – about the size of a silver dollar coin – on the underside of the bird's wings. It is a much more heavily built, dumpy bird than most rollers, with a large red bill. It is a clumsier flier, needing more room than most other rollers to manoeuvre. It is also a very widely spread species. Although resident populations remain in its original home in the Asian tropics – where there are about ten identified geographical races – it has also spread well north and south into temperate regions. These latter populations – in Japan and Korea in the north and in Australia in the south – migrate to south-east Asia and New Guinea, respectively, in winter.

Scientific name	*Eurystomus orientalis*
Family	Coraciidae
Size	28–30cm (11–12in) long
Distribution	Asia and Australasia, from India and Japan to Australia and Solomon Is
Habitat	Open woodland and forest edges; open country with scattered trees
Diet	Large insects, especially beetles, moths and cicadas
Breeding	Nests in tall hollow tree, or in some areas uses old woodpecker or magpie nest; two to four eggs, incubated by both sexes for 18–23 days

Green wood-hoopoe

Wood-hoopoes and hoopoes (*see p.194*) are so distinct from other members of the kingfisher group that they are often placed in a separate order, the Upupiformes. Wood-hoopoes lack the crest of hoopoes, and are mainly tree-living birds. They have a long, narrow, curving bill, and cling like treecreepers (*p.263*) in noisy groups – often upside-down – to the trunk of a tree, searching the bark for insects. Like hoopoes, they smell strongly of musk in the breeding season; their nest holes are dirty and smelly. The green wood-hoopoe is one of the most widespread species, found in wooded country throughout most of sub-Saharan Africa.

Scientific name	*Phoeniculus purpureus*
Family	Upupidae; sometimes classified separately in Phoeniculidae
Size	About 40cm (16in) long
Distribution	Africa south of Sahara
Habitat	Open savannah woodland; acacia bush
Diet	Insects
Breeding	Nests in hollow in tall tree, or in old woodpecker hole; two to four blue eggs, incubated by female for 17–18 days

Hoopoe

With wood-hoopoes (*see p.193*), this species and the related scimitar-bills (genus *Rhinopomastus*) are sometimes classified in a separate order, Upupiformes. The hoopoe is unmistakable with its cinnamon-brown, black and white colouring and prominent crest. It is mainly ground-living, probing with its long bill for small creatures to eat. It can walk and run well (unlike wood-hoopoes, which hop), and flies up into trees to roost. It has unpleasant nesting habits, polluting its hole with droppings and food; the female also has a strong musty smell. Some scientists believe that hoopoes living south of the Sahara comprise several separate species.

Scientific name	*Upupa epops*
Family	Upupidae
Size	About 28cm (11in) long
Distribution	Most of Europe, Asia and Africa except far north and Congo basin
Habitat	Forest edges; open wooded country; orchards; parks; gardens
Diet	Worms, insects and other invertebrates; small lizards
Breeding	Nests in hole in tree, wall or termite mound; up to nine yellowish, greenish or brownish eggs, incubated by female for about 18 days

Great pied or Indian hornbill

A huge bird, the great pied or Indian hornbill (often simply called the great hornbill) is unmistakable. Its large bill is crowned by a horny casque, or 'helmet', almost as big as the bill itself. Hornbills have long been considered fairly close relatives of the hoopoes, but some scientists now believe that they belong in their own order, Bucerotiformes. Apart from their bill, they have unique nesting habits. With the exception of the ground-hornbills (*Bucorvus* species), they nest in hollow trees, but the pair use mud and droppings to almost close the entrance, sealing the female inside. They leave a narrow slit, through which the male feeds his partner until the eggs hatch and she regrows her moulted feathers.

Scientific name	*Buceros bicornis*
Family	Bucerotidae
Size	Male up to 1.5m (5ft) long; female smaller
Distribution	Southern Asia from India and south-west China to Malaya and Sumatra
Habitat	Lowland forests up to 2000m (6500ft)
Diet	Mainly fruits (especially wild figs); insects, lizards and other creatures
Breeding	Pairs for life. Nests in hole in tree, with opening almost sealed (*see above*); one or two eggs, incubated by female for about 30 days

Paradise jacamar

The brightly coloured jacamars, along with the puffbirds (*opposite*) are today often grouped in a separate order, Galbuliformes. Jacamars are slender, graceful birds of the more open forest edges, near roads, clearings and rivers. They perch motionless on a branch until suitable prey comes into view; then they dash out to catch the insect in mid-air with a snap of their bill and return to the perch to eat it. Their narrow bill is not well suited for catching small insects, so they target mainly large dragonflies and butterflies, such as the huge, blue-winged *Morpho* species. Female jacamars look different from males, usually with a brown throat.

Scientific name	*Galbula dea*
Family	Galbulidae
Size	About 30cm (12in) long
Distribution	Parts of Colombia, Venezuela and Guyana; Amazon basin
Habitat	Forest edges and near rivers; upland woodland to 1100m (3600ft)
Diet	Insects, especially butterflies and dragonflies
Breeding	Nests in chamber at end of burrow in bank or steep hillside; three or four eggs, incubated by both sexes for 19–21 days

Collared puffbird

Quite close relatives of the jacamars, the puffbirds are also sometimes grouped in the order Galbuliformes. They are definitely the more dowdy members of the group, usually being much less colourful and lacking the jacamars' sleek build. They have a rather large head, short neck and flattened, heavy bill. This last is, however, much better suited to catching small insects in mid-air than the jacamars'. Puffbirds like to sit on a branch, waiting for suitable prey, with their thick neck and body feathers fluffed out – hence the English name. Some species, with particularly drab brown or black plumage, are known as monklets, nunlets and nunbirds.

Scientific name	*Bucco capensis*
Family	Bucconidae
Size	About 18cm (7in) long
Distribution	Amazon and parts of Orinoco basins of South America
Habitat	Lowland rainforest, to 1000m (3300ft)
Diet	Insects
Breeding	Nests in burrow in bank, or sloping into level ground; two to three eggs, believed to be incubated by both sexes

Coppersmith barbet

The name barbet refers to the fringe of bristles around these stocky birds' short, heavy bill. There are 26 Asian species, another 42 in Africa (now in the separate family Lybiidae) and 14 American barbets included in the toucan family (*see p.200*). Many have ringing, metallic-sounding, monotonous calls, and the coppersmith's sounds very much like the 'tonk' of a hammer striking a sheet of metal. (In Rudyard Kipling's *Jungle Book*, Darzee the coppersmith is 'the town-crier to every Indian garden'.) Also known as the crimson-breasted barbet, it is a brightly coloured bird, but it tends to hide among the leaves of trees so is heard much more than seen.

Scientific name	*Megalaima haemacephala*
Family	Capitonidae; now often classified in separate family, Megalaimidae
Size	About 16cm (6¼in) long
Distribution	Asia from Pakistan to southern China, Indonesia and Philippines
Habitat	Open woodland, farmland and gardens, to 2000m (6500ft)
Diet	Mainly fruits, especially wild figs; some insects
Breeding	Nests in hole dug in dead or rotting tree-trunk or branch, or in termite mound; two to four eggs, incubated by both sexes for 13–15 days

Greater or black-throated honeyguide

Honeyguides are so called because they indicate the presence of a nearby wild bees' nest. The best-known species, the greater honeyguide, has evolved an extraordinary strategy for getting its favourite foods: honey, beeswax and bees. With its chattering call and short flights, it leads a person or an animal such as a honey badger (ratel) to a nest, waits for the nest to be broken open and then later feeds on the leftovers. Honeyguides are unique in being able to digest beeswax, helped by special micro-organisms in their intestines. They are also among the few birds apart from cuckoos (*see pp.153–156*) that lay their eggs in another bird's nest.

Scientific name	*Indicator indicator*
Family	Indicatoridae
Size	About 20cm (8in) long
Distribution	Most of sub-Saharan Africa
Habitat	Wooded savannah and dry woodland; forest edge; farmland
Diet	Honey, wax, bees and larvae from bees' nests; other insects
Breeding	Nest parasite. Lays single egg in nest of hole-nesting species such as barbet or woodpecker, which incubates it; hatchling kills other nestlings

Toco toucan

With their comical-looking giant bill – less unwieldy than it looks, in fact, since it has a honeycomb structure and is quite light – toucans are instantly recognizable. They look ungainly in flight, but hop nimbly along branches, picking fruits with the tip of their bill and then tossing them back to swallow them. The toco toucan has the biggest bill of all, 20cm (8in) in length, and is the species best known through advertising and illustrations. The evolutionary significance of such a long bill is unclear. It lets the bird reach for inaccessible fruits, but other bird species have no such problems. It may have more to do with intimidating other birds, whose eggs and nestlings toucans sometimes steal.

Scientific name	*Ramphastos toco*
Family	Ramphastidae
Size	About 64cm (25in) long
Distribution	Eastern South America, from Guyana to northern Argentina
Habitat	Lowland forest, woodland and plantations (mostly in upper layers)
Diet	Mainly fruits; also insects and other small creatures; eggs and nestlings
Breeding	Nests in natural hollow in tree; two to four eggs, incubated by both sexes for about 18 days

Plate-billed mountain-toucan

A toucan's massive bill is usually colourful, but this species surpasses most. It has an extra, bright yellow horny plate – of unknown purpose – on the side of each upper mandible. Yellow and greenish-blue patches around the eyes, blue-grey underparts with a yellow patch on each flank, and red undertail feathers all add to the gaudy effect. Its upper parts are mostly brown. Its plumage has a fine, hairy texture. It is one of four mountain-toucan species that live high in the northern Andes of South America, and the only one found on the western slopes. The birds move up and down the mountains according to the seasonal availability of fruits, calling loudly as they look for food in pairs or small groups.

Scientific name	*Andigena laminirostris*
Family	Ramphastidae
Size	About 50cm (20in) long
Distribution	Andes of western Colombia and Ecuador
Habitat	Humid mountain forest, at 300–3200m (1000–10 500ft)
Diet	Forest fruits; insects
Breeding	Nests in natural hollow in tree; two to four eggs, incubated by both sexes for about 15–16 days

Red-necked araçari

The araçaris are a group of 13 rather slender-bodied and slender-billed toucan species that live in warm, humid forests from southern Mexico to northern Argentina. They are better fliers and more sociable than other toucans, flying through the forests in flocks. They are also unusual in roosting at night in tree hollows, as well as using such holes for raising their young. All toucans have to 'fold' themselves to fit into such holes: they turn their head to lay the bill over their back, then fold the tail feathers up and over the bill. The red-necked (or double-collared) araçari is gaudily coloured, like most araçaris. One species, the curl-crested araçari (*Pteroglossus beauharnaesii*) has glossy, curly head feathers.

Scientific name	*Pteroglossus bitorquatus*
Family	Ramphastidae
Size	About 38cm (15in) long
Distribution	Amazon basin of Brazil and eastern Bolivia
Habitat	Lowland rainforest
Diet	Mainly forest fruits
Breeding	Nests in natural hollow in tree or in old woodpecker hole; two to four eggs, incubated by both sexes for about 15–16 days

Eurasian or northern wryneck

The name wryneck refers to this small bird's unique, snake-like neck-twisting and swaying action – accompanied by a hissing sound – when it or its nestlings are threatened by a predator. It is a well-camouflaged, rather dull-looking bird that is quite different in appearance and habits from other members of the woodpecker family. It perches across a branch rather than along it (although it can also cling to a tree-trunk), and its bill is too short and weak to bore a nesting hole for itself or to get food. But it does use its long, sticky, fast-moving tongue to pick up insects – ants are its favourite food – and larvae from the ground or from leaves or branches.

Scientific name	*Jynx torquilla*
Family	Picidae
Size	About 16.5cm (6½in) long
Distribution	Northern Eurasia from Britain to Japan; winters in Africa, southern Asia
Habitat	Open woodland; orchards; wooded farmland; parks
Diet	Ants and other insects and larvae
Breeding	Nests in existing hole in tree (including woodpecker hole), bank or wall; six to nine eggs, incubated mainly by female for 12–14 days

Guianan or arrowhead piculet

Piculets are tiny birds, but they do use their bill in woodpecker fashion – to drum on a branch or tree-trunk during the breeding season, to probe the bark for insects and their larvae to eat (catching them with their long tongue), and to excavate a nesting hole in soft or rotting wood. But they lack the true woodpeckers' stiff tail. They are very active birds, clambering and hopping among the branches and foliage of trees, often hanging upside-down rather like a tit or nuthatch (*see pp.259–262*), as they forage for food. Despite its scientific name, the Guianan piculet is not the very smallest species; some piculets are no more than 7.5cm (3in) long.

Scientific name	*Picnumnus minutissimus*
Family	Picidae
Size	About 10cm (4in) long
Distribution	North-eastern South America
Habitat	Forest edge; savannah; woods (including swamp forests)
Diet	Insects and larvae
Breeding	Nests in small hole (including enlarged existing hole) in soft or rotten tree-trunk; two to four eggs, incubated for 11–14 days

Northern or yellow-shafted flicker

The flicker is an unusual, mainly ground-living woodpecker that walks rather than hops. It feeds mostly on the ground – often plunging its bill into an ant's nest to pick up insects with its sticky tongue – but chisels its nesting hole in a tree like other woodpeckers. There are two, closely related but distinctive forms that most ornithologists consider subspecies of the same species. The yellow-shafted flicker illustrated has yellow shafts to the wing and tail feathers, and lives in the eastern part of the bird's range. In the west is the red-shafted flicker, a subspecies with red shafts. Where their territories overlap there are intermediate forms.

Scientific name	*Colaptes auratus*
Family	Picidae
Size	25–35cm (10–14in) long
Distribution	Alaska and most of Canada to Nicaragua and parts of Caribbean
Habitat	Forest; open woodland; parks and gardens
Diet	Ants and other ground-living insects; some fruits and berries
Breeding	Excavates nesting hole in dead tree-trunk or branch; usually about four eggs, incubated by both sexes for about 12 days

Crimson-winged woodpecker

The crimson-winged woodpecker of south-east Asia is one of the most vividly coloured of all true woodpeckers, with its olive-green back, crimson and black wing feathers, red head and yellow crest (which is shown lowered in the illustration but is raised prominently when a male is displaying to a female). Like all true woodpeckers, its feet are well adapted to climbing tree-trunks as it searches for insects and probes the bark for wood-boring larvae. Two toes point forward and two back, and the fourth (outer) toe on each foot can be turned sideways for the best grip. At the same time, the strong wedge-shaped tail feathers prop up its body.

Scientific name	*Picus puniceus*
Family	Picidae
Size	About 25cm (10in) long
Distribution	South-eastern Asia – Thailand, Burma, Malaysia, Indonesia
Habitat	Upper levels of lowland forests and woodland, to 900m (3000ft)
Diet	Mainly insects and their larvae (especially ants and termites)
Breeding	Nests in hole usually excavated high up in dead tree-trunk; two or three eggs; incubation period uncertain

Black woodpecker

The biggest woodpecker in Europe (but rare in Britain), the black woodpecker may be mistaken for a crow or jackdaw (*see p.311*). It is all black except for the red crown. This colouring plays an important part in terrtorial displays between rival males, when each waves his head with the bill pointing upwards. Such a 'tournament' may last for more than an hour before one bird gives up. A similar, though briefer, threat display occurs between males and females, but because the female's red patch is much smaller the male bird's aggression quickly wanes. Black woodpeckers 'drum' very loudly during courtship, beating their bill against a tree as many as 43 times in a period of 2½ seconds.

Scientific name	*Dryocopus martius*
Family	Picidae
Size	45–47cm (17½–18½in) long
Distribution	Most of continental Europe and Asia north of Himalayas
Habitat	Forest, mostly to 1000m (3300ft); to 4300m (14 000ft) in Tibet and China
Diet	Tree-living insects, especially certain ants; larvae
Breeding	Excavates nesting hole in tree-trunk (used for up to six years); usually three to five eggs, incubated by both sexes for 12–14 days

Great spotted woodpecker

The spotted wing pattern of this, the most common European woodpecker, is less apparent when the wings are folded so that the spots form white bars. It has red undertail feathers, and juveniles have a red crown, but mature female birds lack the red band at the back of the male's head. Great spotted woodpeckers are very adaptable, living in many types of woodland over a wide geographical range. Most stay in their territory all year, but some far northern populations may migrate south in winter. They use their bill in typical woodpecker fashion, for drumming, for chiselling into bark and wood, and also to prise open pine cones for their seeds.

Scientific name	*Dendrocopus major*
Family	Picidae
Size	22–23cm (8½–9in) long
Distribution	Much of Europe and Asia
Habitat	Forests, woodland, farmland, parks and gardens to 2300m (7500ft)
Diet	Mainly wood-boring insects and larvae; some nuts, seeds and berries
Breeding	Excavates nesting hole in dead tree-trunk; three to eight eggs, incubated by both sexes (but mainly female) for about 16 days

Ivory-billed woodpecker

Many ornithologists believe, or fear, that the ivory-billed woodpecker – North America's biggest woodpecker – is now extinct. It was never common, but once lived in many areas of hardwood forest that have now been destroyed. The last proven sighting was in Cuba in the late 1980s. A graduate student claimed to have watched a pair for some time in Louisiana in 1999, and an official 30-day search in the area in 2002 found evidence of the bird and heard what could have been its distinctive tapping sound – but no solid proof of its continued survival. Most claimed sightings are of the similar though smaller pileated woodpecker (*Dryocopus pileatus*), which has a darker bill and lacks white wing feathers.

Scientific name	*Campephilus principalis*
Family	Picidae
Size	About 50cm (20in) long
Distribution	Formerly much of southern and south-eastern United States; Cuba
Habitat	Mature deciduous forest and cypress swamps (large territory)
Diet	Mainly wood-boring insects and larvae; also other insects, fruits, seeds
Breeding	Nest cavity excavated by both sexes in dead tree; up to three eggs, incubated by both sexes for about 20 days

Red-headed woodpecker

Once much more common than it is today, the red-headed woodpecker is still very widespread in eastern North America but since the 1890s has suffered from competition for nesting holes from introduced European starlings (*see p.294*). Its entirely red head, neck and throat makes it distinctive. Like other woodpeckers, it digs for wood-boring insects in the bark of trees, but more often it darts out to catch flying insects or forages for food on the ground. It eats many seeds, and stores much of the food it collects for later use in crevices or holes, sometimes using wood chips to hide it from scavengers. Northern birds often migrate south in winter.

Scientific name	*Melanerpes erythrocephalus*
Family	Picidae
Size	21–25cm (8–10in) long
Distribution	Most of North America east of the Rockies
Habitat	Open woodland; farmland; parks and gardens
Diet	Flying, ground-living and wood-boring insects; seeds, berries and fruits
Breeding	Excavates nesting hole in dead tree-trunk or telegraph pole; usually four or five eggs, incubated by both sexes for 12–13 days

Banded broadbill

Broadbills are some of the most primitive birds in the order (major group) Passeriformes. This group, also known as perching birds (although they are not the only birds that perch), songbirds (although not all of them sing) or passerines ('sparrow-like'), includes more than half of all known bird species. Broadbills are rather plump birds with a heavy bill that is hooked at the tip. There are two main groups; most broadbills are largely insectivorous, but green broadbills eat fruit and berries. Both types build an intricate and superbly camouflaged egg- or pear-shaped nest, with a small entrance hole, that dangles from a branch, often over a stream.

Scientific name	*Eurylaimus javanicus*
Family	Eurylaimidae
Size	details unknown
Distribution	South-eastern Asia – Burma; Thailand; Indochina; Malaysia; Indonesia
Habitat	Lowland forest and woodland, to 1000m (3300ft)
Diet	Mainly insects; some small frogs and lizards
Breeding	Egg- or pear-shaped nest of plant fibres, hanging from tree branch or climbing plant; two to five eggs; details of incubation unknown

Red-billed scythebill

The scythebill is one of about 50 species of the woodcreeper family living in Central and South America. They are the New World equivalents of (but are unrelated to) the treecreepers (see *p.263*), and specialize in creeping up the trunk of trees, probing the bark and crevices for insects to eat. The long, curved bill of the scythebill is also ideal for catching insects in the tubular flowers and the vase shape formed by the overlapping leaves of bromeliads (plants of the pineapple family), which grow perched on the branches of forest trees. Woodcreepers are hole-nesters, and some species even signal their mates by drumming their bill on hollow trees. But the bill is too weak to chisel a hole, so they use existing hollows as nests.

Scientific name	*Campylorhamphus trochilirostris*
Family	Dendrocolaptidae
Size	20–30cm (8–12in) long, including 8cm (3in) bill
Distribution	Much of eastern South America, from Panama to Argentina
Habitat	Rainforest, swampy woodland and deciduous forest to 2000m (6500ft)
Diet	Insects
Breeding	Nests in natural hollow in tree or stump, or in old woodpecker nest; two or three eggs, incubated by both sexes for about 15 days

Sharp-tailed streamcreeper

The streamcreeper is a member of a large group of Central and South American birds known as ovenbirds, after the best-known species, the rufous ovenbird or hornero (*Furnarius rufus*), which builds a domed mud nest like a clay oven. The names of many other species describe their food-searching habits: earthcreeper, treerunner, leaftosser, foliage-gleaner. The sharp-tailed streamcreeper hops along quiet forest streams, flicking leaves for insects, its tail upraised. However, the bird is also found in city outskirts, where its habit of nesting in rat-holes beside open sewers has earned it a less polite nickname among shanty-dwellers: 'captain of filth'.

Scientific name	*Lochmias nematura*
Family	Furnariidae
Size	details unknown
Distribution	South America, from Panama to Paraguay and Argentina
Habitat	Humid forests and undergrowth along streams; towns and cities
Diet	Mainly insects and other small creatures
Breeding	Nests in burrow (often former rodent burrow) in bank of stream or ditch; other details of eggs and incubation unknown

Barred antshrike

The antshrikes live mainly among the undergrowth and lower branches of forest trees. They are continually searching for insects, usually in pairs which chatter and call to each other with descending trills in order to keep in touch in the dense vegetation. Despite their name, they – like most of their cousins the antbirds – are not particularly fond of ants; the group got its name because some of its members take advantage of the insect life disturbed by marching columns of forest ants. In most of the group males and females are different; the female barred antshrike is mainly brown. Both have a crest – kept partly erect in the male – and a toothed bill.

Scientific name	*Thamnophilus doliatus*
Family	Formicariidae; sometimes classified in separate family, Thamnophilidae
Size	About 15cm (6in) long
Distribution	Americas from Mexico to Argentina, east of Andes; Trinidad
Habitat	Thickets, scrub, savannah, mangroves and towns, to 2000m (6500ft)
Diet	Insects, including beetles and caterpillars; berries
Breeding	Deep cup-shaped nest on low branch of tree; two or three eggs, incubated by both sexes (only female at night) for 15–16 days

Great kiskadee

A member of the tyrant flycatcher family, the great kiskadee (sometimes called the Derby flycatcher) is named after its loud 'kiss-ka-dee' call. Several species of flycatchers with similar colouring live in tropical Central and South America, but no other species like it ranges as far north as Texas and Bermuda (where it has been common since the 1950s). Like other flycatchers, the kiskadee often flies out from a perch to catch flying insects, but it also forages on the ground for worms and other small creatures, takes small lizards from rocks or tree-trunks, eats berries and seeds in winter, raids other birds' nests, and will even dive into water for fish or frogs.

Scientific name	*Pitangus sulphuratus*
Family	Tyrannidae
Size	23–27cm (9–10½in) long
Distribution	Americas, Texas to Argentina (east of Andes); Bermuda (introduced)
Habitat	Open woodland; savannah; towns; usually found near water
Diet	Flying and terrestrial insects; worms; small vertebrates (including fish)
Breeding	Bulky domed nest of twigs and weeds with side entrance, in fork of tree; two to five (usually four) glossy eggs, incubation details unknown

Fork-tailed flycatcher

Two rather similar long-tailed species of tyrant flycatchers live in overlapping territories, both sometimes called the swallow-tailed flycatcher. The fork-tailed species is native from Mexico southwards, but often strays into the eastern United States; it has a black head with a small yellow or whitish patch on the crown. The scissor-tailed flycatcher (*Tyrannus forficata*) breeds in south-central USA and winters from Texas to Panama; it has pinkish flanks and a pale grey head. Both feed in the same way as the unrelated European flycatchers (*see p.257*), by darting out from a low perch – often a telephone or fence wire – to catch insects in mid-air.

Scientific name	*Tyrannus savana* or *Muscivora tyrannus*
Family	Tyrannidae
Size	38–40cm (15–16in) long, including tail; juveniles' tail much shorter
Distribution	Central and South America, from Mexico to Argentina, east of Andes
Habitat	Open lowlands to 2600m (8500ft) – mainly savannah, scrub, farmland
Diet	Flying insects; some fruit
Breeding	Shallow cup-shaped nest of plant materials in tree or bush; usually two to four eggs, incubated by female for about 16 days

White-bearded manakin

Manakins are tiny, chubby, lively birds that move through the forest searching for insects and berries to eat. In most species the females are olive-green, while the males are black with white or colourful patches. Males and females generally have separate territories, the male's including a special display ground, or lek, that he clears. The male white-bearded manakin displays to attract females by flying between two saplings, his 'beard' puffed out, while making clicking and whirring noises with his wings. The female joins him in the dance, and they mate on a perch. The female then builds a nest, lays her eggs, incubates them, and raises the young.

Scientific name	*Manacus manacus*
Family	Pipridae; sometimes included in Tyrannidae
Size	About 11cm (4½in) long
Distribution	South America west of Andes, from Colombia to northern Argentina
Habitat	Open woodland, forest edge and undergrowth, to 1900m (6200ft)
Diet	Small berries; insects, mainly caught on foliage
Breeding	Frail cup-shaped nest of grass and plant fibres, built by female on low branch; two eggs, incubated by female for 13–15 days

Swallow-tailed manakin

The swallow-tailed (or blue) manakin is one of the longest species, but virtually all the extra length is due to the tail; the bird's body is just as compact and chubby as in other manakins. The male is a beautiful blue and black colour with a bright red or orange crown, the female green. Males clear leks (display grounds) to attract and display to females, like other species, but the swallow-tail and its close relatives are unique in the way 'rival' males cooperate. They dance up and down a low bough, skilfully changing places, while making rattling and buzzing noises; yet only one chosen male will be able to mate with the female that they jointly attract.

Scientific name	*Chiroxiphia caudata*
Family	Pipridae; sometimes included in Tyrannidae
Size	About 15cm (6in) long
Distribution	South-eastern Brazil; southern Paraguay; north-eastern Argentina
Habitat	Lowland forest
Diet	Small fruits and berries; insects
Breeding	Frail cup-shaped nest of grass and plant fibres, built by female in fork of bush branch; two eggs, incubated by female for 13–15 days

Guianan cock-of-the-rock

The cotingas form a very diverse family – some are brilliantly coloured, others quite drab – but the cocks-of-the-rock are the showiest of all. There are two species: the orange Guianan cock-of-the-rock of lowland forests in South America's north-east, and the soft red Andean or Peruvian species (*Rupicola peruviana*) of the high Andes gorges. Both make unique bracket-shaped mud nests attached to a rock face. Males of both species make elaborate group courtship displays to females in a cleared 'court' or lek in the forest, like the manakins (*see pp.217–218*). They spread their brilliant plumage and turn their head to show off their fan-like topknot.

Scientific name	*Rupicola rupicola*
Family	Cotingidae; sometimes included in Tyrannidae
Size	About 30cm (12in) long
Distribution	Colombia (east of Andes) and Venezuela to northern Brazil
Habitat	Lowland forest and open woodland, usually near rock outcrop
Diet	Fruits; small creatures
Breeding	Cup-shaped nest of mud, plant fibres and saliva, made by female and attached like bracket to rock; two eggs, incubated for 23–28 days

Amazonian or ornate umbrella-bird

Another member of the cotinga family with an extraordinary head-dress, the umbrella-bird is rather crow-like in body and build. However, it has an erect crest of long silky feathers on its head and a long wattle or lappet hanging from its neck. Both are much larger in the male than the female; the male expands his crest like a parasol when performing his courtship display. In the Amazonian, or ornate, umbrella-bird, the male's wattle grows up to 33cm (13in) long and is covered with feathers. Another form – which may be a separate species or a subspecies of the Amazonian – has a bright red unfeathered wattle. These birds live in the top of forest trees, and the male displays from a favourite perch.

Scientific name	*Cephalopterus ornatus*
Family	Cotingidae; sometimes included in Tyrannidae
Size	40–45cm (16–18in) long
Distribution	Northern parts of South America, east of Andes
Habitat	Canopy level of lowland humid forest, to 1200m (3900ft)
Diet	Fruits; some insects
Breeding	Shallow twiggy nest in fork of tree; single egg, incubated by female (incubation period uncertain)

Bearded bellbird

The four species of bellbirds are named after the loud 'clanging' call – like a hammer striking an anvil or bell – that the males make from a favourite perch to advertise their presence to females and other males. One of the loudest of all bird calls, it can carry as far as 1km (1100yd) through the jungle. In all four species, the male has white or partially white plumage – an unusual colour for forest birds. The bearded bellbird (also called the black-winged bellbird) has a fringe of thin black wattles – the 'beard' – hanging below the bill of both sexes. Only the male has black wings and brown head; the female is a soft olive-green with yellow markings. The birds live in the lower layers of the forest.

Scientific name	*Procnias averano*
Family	Cotingidae; sometimes included in Tyrannidae
Size	About 25cm (10in) long
Distribution	Northern parts of South America, east of Andes
Habitat	Lowland humid forest and woodland, to 1600m (5250ft)
Diet	Mainly fruits and large berries, especially laurel
Breeding	Thin cup-shaped nest of twigs built by female on forked branch of tree; single egg, incubated by female for about 23 days

Lovely cotinga

The name 'lovely' is well deserved, at least as far as the male is concerned, for this bird's plumage is a beautiful combination of lavender or purple (due to the same pigment, cotingin, as in the Pompadour cotinga, *opposite*) and sky-blue. The female, on the other hand, is a rather drab brown colour with markings that give good camouflage against the forest foliage. The lovely cotinga is a bird of the forest canopy, and also the more open forest edges. In the breeding season, males make an airborne display, with whirring wings, among the treetops. As with other members of the family, the female is believed to build a nest and raise her single young alone.

Scientific name	*Cotinga amabilis*
Family	Cotingidae; sometimes included in Tyrannidae
Size	About 19cm (7½in) long
Distribution	Eastern Central America, from southern Mexico to Costa Rica
Habitat	Humid forest and woodland
Diet	Mainly fruits; some insects
Breeding	Shallow cup nest of vegetation, built by female in tree; single egg, incubated by female (incubation period uncertain)

Pompadour cotinga

The first specimen of this bird to reach Europe and be described scientifically was part of a batch of brightly coloured bird skins sent in the mid-18th century from Guiana to the French courtesan Madame de Pompadour. She was known for her flamboyant hairstyles, decorated with ribbons, feathers and even complete birds. The shipment was captured by the British navy, but the British naturalist who published a description of the bird gallantly named it after Madame de Pompadour. The rich purple colouring of the male's plumage is caused by a pigment (colouring material) in the feathers known as cotingin; it is found only in certain cotingas.

Scientific name	*Xipholena punicea*
Family	Cotingidae; sometimes included in Tyrannidae
Size	About 20cm (8in) long
Distribution	Northern parts of South America, east of Andes
Habitat	Lowland forest, to 1300m (4250ft)
Diet	Mainly fruits; some insects
Breeding	Small cup-shaped nest of twigs, built in tree by female; single egg, incubated by female (incubation period uncertain)

White-tipped plantcutter

Three species of plantcutters live in temperate South America. They have small serrations, or teeth, on the sides of the bill which help them to pluck and strip succulent foliage from plants. They are the only family of the Passeriformes known to depend on plant stems, buds and leaves as their main food. All three species are somewhat similar in the males' reddish colouring, the females being a duller ochre or brownish colour; all have white wing bars. The white-tipped plantcutter is the most brightly coloured species, with white tips to the tail feathers. It migrates from southern thornbush to spend winters in bushy grassland pasture farther north.

Scientific name	*Phytotoma rutila*
Family	Phytotomidae; sometimes included in Tyrannidae
Size	About 18cm (7in) long
Distribution	Parts of Bolivia, Paraguay, Uruguay and Argentina
Habitat	Temperate woodland and scrub
Diet	Buds; young leaves; fruits; seeds
Breeding	Untidy shallow nest of twigs built in thick, thorny bush or cactus; two to four eggs, incubated by female (incubation period uncertain)

Giant pitta

Brightly coloured, rather plump small birds – even the 'giant' species is not particularly big compared with many birds – the pittas are mostly ground-living forest species. They are found in southern and south-east Asia, with a few species in tropical Africa. Some species have very different males and females, but the female giant pitta is much like the male except for a rusty-brown head and underparts. They are difficult to spot among the dense undergrowth where they feed, but roost at night in the branches of trees. Pittas' olfactory (smell) system is among the most highly developed of all songbirds', and they probably find their food by smell.

Scientific name	*Pitta caerulea*
Family	Pittidae
Size	About 28cm (11in) long
Distribution	Malay peninsula; Sumatra; Borneo
Habitat	Lowland forest, to 1200m (4000ft)
Diet	Mainly earthworms and snails
Breeding	Domed nest of twigs and leaves, with side entrance, in undergrowth; three to five almost round eggs, incubated by both sexes for 15–17 days

False sunbird, or sunbird-asity

This tiny, secretive bird – one of only four species in its family, one of which may well be extinct – seems to be a descendant of a primitive group of birds that has long died out elsewhere in the world. It is so similar to the true sunbirds (*see pp.264–265*) – with its curved bill, tubular tongue (for sipping nectar) and twice-yearly moult – that it was long thought to be a member of the same family. Its only close relatives are now known to be the bigger, pitta-like asities (*Philepitta* species). The glittering blue back plumage shown in the illustration is seen only on the male during the breeding season; at other times, both male and female are olive-green.

Scientific name	*Neodrepanis coruscans*
Family	Philepittidae
Size	9–10cm (3½–4in) long
Distribution	North-western and eastern Madagascar
Habitat	Rainforest and woodland
Diet	Probably nectar; small insects
Breeding	Habits unknown, although related velvet asity (*Philepitta castanea*)
	builds pear-shaped mossy nest hanging from branch

Superb lyrebird

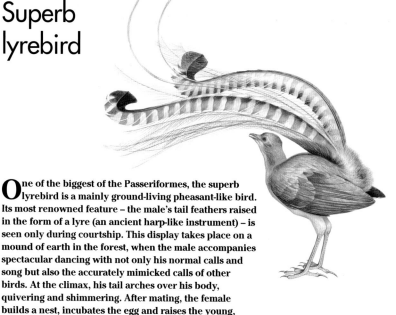

One of the biggest of the Passeriformes, the superb lyrebird is a mainly ground-living pheasant-like bird. Its most renowned feature – the male's tail feathers raised in the form of a lyre (an ancient harp-like instrument) – is seen only during courtship. This display takes place on a mound of earth in the forest, when the male accompanies spectacular dancing with not only his normal calls and song but also the accurately mimicked calls of other birds. At the climax, his tail arches over his body, quivering and shimmering. After mating, the female builds a nest, incubates the egg and raises the young, while the male may mate with several other females.

Scientific name	*Menura novaehollandiae*
Family	Menuridae
Size	Male up to 1m (3ft 3in) long, including tail; female up to 86cm (34in)
Distribution	Coastal zone of south-eastern Australia; introduced in Tasmania
Habitat	Temperate and subtropical rainforest; tree-fern gullies
Diet	Insects, worms, snails and other small ground creatures
Breeding	Polygynous. Female builds large dome-shaped nest of sticks and other
	vegetation; single purplish egg, incubated by female for 40–50 days

Skylark

The lark family is the first among the Passeriformes to truly deserve the name songbirds, and the Eurasian skylark is justly renowned for its sweet warbling song, delivered as the bird flutters higher and higher in the air. The song proclaims its territory, and is heard during the breeding season and especially in the early morning; in other seasons, skylarks live in communal flocks. Its favourite home is the short grass of pastures, where it nests and roosts on the ground, crouching when disturbed. But it will often perch on a wall or fence. It walks rather than hops, and enjoys dust-baths. Northern populations may migrate southwards in winter.

Scientific name	*Alauda arvensis*
Family	Alaudidae
Size	About 18cm (7in) long
Distribution	Europe; northern North Africa; much of Asia; introduced elsewhere
Habitat	Heaths; grassland; fields; moorland; marshes
Diet	Seeds; plant material; ground-living insects and other invertebrates
Breeding	Cup-shaped nest of grass in hollow, well hidden among grasses; three to six speckled eggs, incubated mainly by female for 11–12 days

Shore or horned lark

The only lark native to North America (where the skylark is an introduced species in some areas), there are about 40 recognized geographical races or subspecies of this bird, many of them isolated and/or migratory. For example, it is resident (present all year) in the mountains of the Balkans. But it is a summer visitor to Scandinavia, the Eurasian tundra, and alpine meadows and tundra in northern North America, migrating to the south, to temperate shores and lowland fields, in winter. It is quite easily recognized by the black and yellow head pattern, but loses the characteristic tiny black 'horns' in winter. It makes shrill 'tseep-tseep' calls.

Scientific name	*Eremophila alpestris*
Family	Alaudidae
Size	16–17cm (about 6½in) long
Distribution	Parts of Americas, Europe, Asia and North Africa; migratory (*see above*)
Habitat	Alpine meadows to 5200m (17 000ft); tundra; steppes; beaches; fields
Diet	Seeds; buds; insects and larvae; small crustaceans and molluscs
Breeding	Cup-shaped nest of plant materials in hollow on ground; usually about four eggs, incubated mainly by female for about 12 days

Swallow

Known widely as the barn swallow because it often nests in outbuildings, this bird is a well-known summer visitor almost everywhere except New Zealand, most of Australia and the coldest parts of the major continents. Each year, swallows fly thousands of kilometres in large flocks between Northern Hemisphere breeding sites and the Southern Hemisphere where they spend the northern winter. They are superb, fast fliers, with a streamlined body and long tail streamers; they look similar to swifts (*see p.172*), but are not related. Like swifts, they catch flying insects in their wide gape, and also swoop down to skim water to drink and to catch surface insects.

Scientific name	*Hirundo rustica*
Family	Hirundinidae
Size	19–22cm (7½–8½in) long
Distribution	Virtually worldwide except far north and south; migratory (*see above*)
Habitat	Open country near water, with buildings; towns and villages
Diet	Flying and floating insects, especially flies and mosquitoes
Breeding	Nest of mud and straw under roof or on wall ledge (originally on cliff or in cave); four or five eggs, incubated mainly by female for 14–16 days

Sand martin, or bank swallow

One of the smallest swallows – there is no real difference between 'swallows' and 'martins' – the sand martin is a rather drab bird. But it has slender, powerful wings and is an energetic and skilful flier, darting and twisting in the air to catch flying insects. It is also almost as widespread as the swallow, migrating between the Northern Hemisphere (where it breeds) and South America, Africa, northern India and south-east Asia for the northern winter months. Both male and female help to dig their nesting burrow, up to 1m (3ft 3in) deep in a bank, often next to a river, lake, road or railway line. They use their bill to loosen the earth, then kick it free.

Scientific name	*Riparia riparia*
Family	Hirundinidae
Size	About 12cm (4½–5in) long
Distribution	Almost worldwide except far north and south; migratory (*see above*)
Habitat	Open country with steep sand or gravel banks, near water
Diet	Flying insects
Breeding	Nests in chamber at end of burrow dug in bank (often used in successive years); usually four or five eggs, incubated by both sexes for 15–16 days

231

White wagtail

The wagtails are so called because of their habit of continually wagging their long tail up and down as they run over the ground, searching for insects. They often break into flight from a run in order to catch a low-flying insect. There are several subspecies of white wagtail apart from the grey-backed continental European form illustrated. The British subspecies, *Motacilla alba yarrellii*, is known as the pied wagtail; it is entirely black and white. Another form, *M.a. subpersonata*, found in Morocco, has even more black on the head. All have a white chin in winter. White wagtails are resident in some areas but migrate south from cold regions in winter.

Scientific name	*Motacilla alba*
Family	Motacillidae
Size	17–18cm (6½–7in) long
Distribution	Europe; Africa; Asia; western Alsaka; partial migrant (*see above*)
Habitat	Open country, usually but not always near water; common near houses
Diet	Mainly insects
Breeding	Cup-shaped nest of grass, usually in hollow on ground, or in crevice in scree or wall; five or six eggs, incubated by both sexes for about 15 days

Meadow pipit

Pipits are similar to wagtails, but are generally slightly plumper and have rather inconspicuous, usually brown plumage, often with heavy camouflage streaking. They are also rather similar to larks (*see pp.228–229*), and are sometimes known as fieldlarks or titlarks. The meadow pipit is widespread on grassland and moors from Greenland to Central Asia. Like the skylark, it makes a song-flight over its territory during the breeding season, trilling (although much less musically than the skylark) as it rises then slowly descends to the ground; it sings similarly from a post or bush. Birds in cold-climate areas migrate to North Africa and the Middle East in winter.

Scientific name	*Anthus pratensis*
Family	Motacillidae
Size	About 15cm (6in) long
Distribution	Greenland; Europe; western Asia; partial migrant (*see above*)
Habitat	Moorland; heaths; grassland; meadows; marshes; tundra
Diet	Mainly insects
Breeding	Cup-shaped nest of grass in hollow on ground, usually hidden by bush
	or tussock; four or five eggs, incubated by female for about 15 days

Red-whiskered bulbul

Bulbuls are generally noisy, active and gregarious birds, and the red-whiskered species is no exception. It is named after the tufts of bright red feathers on each cheek. The undertail feathers are also red, and the bird has a pronounced black crest. It is a common garden bird in such cities as Sydney and Melbourne in Australia and Miami in Florida, and in Hawaii – where in each case it is an introduced species – and, closer to its normal range, in Singapore. However, its liking for green and ripening fruit and buds means that it is regarded by fruit-farmers as a pest. It makes characteristically short, jerky flights from tree to tree as it searches for food, and makes short, bright, musical calls.

Scientific name	*Pycnonotus jacosus*
Family	Pycnonotidae
Size	About 20cm (8in) long
Distribution	India; south-east Asia; southern China; introduced in Australia and USA
Habitat	Woodland; scrub; cultivated land; orchards; parks; gardens
Diet	Fruits; berries; buds; insects
Breeding	Cup-shaped nest of plant materials built in fork of tree or bush; two to four eggs, incubated by both sexes for 11–14 days

Asian fairy bluebird

This beautiful bird is a member of the leafbird family, a rather poorly understood Asian group. It is quite common in its range but is shy, and is clearly seen only when it comes down to the ground for water. At other times, it lives mainly high in forest trees, where the male's black underparts make it difficult to spot. The female is less colourful than the male, with green and brown plumage. Fairy bluebirds have a melodious, fluent song, and males make striking aerial displays at breeding times. Their relatives the leafbirds (*Chloropsis* species) are smaller, mainly bright green birds also of the forest canopy; while ioras (*Aegithina* species) are also green but feed on insects at forest edges and in gardens.

Scientific name	*Irena puella*
Family	Irenidae; sometimes listed as Chloropseidae
Size	About 26.5cm (10½in) long
Distribution	Parts of India; south-east Asia to Java, Borneo and Philippines
Habitat	Upland forest, to 1700m (5500ft)
Diet	Fruits (especially wild figs); nectar
Breeding	Shallow nest of twigs and moss on branch of young tree deep in forest; usually two streaked eggs (incubation period uncertain)

Northern or great grey shrike

Shrikes are the most predatory of the Passeriformes, the songbird counterparts to owls or even hawks. They are in fact largely insect-eaters, but many species – the northern or great grey shrike among them – also take small warm-blooded animals. Like many shrikes it keeps watch for prey from a high perch, then swoops to catch it in mid-air or on the ground; it sometimes hovers like a hawk when hunting. The bird usually returns to its perch to eat the catch with its strong, hooked bill, but may impale it on a thorn or barbed wire to eat later; such a 'larder' of impaled prey is a good sign of shrikes around. Northern populations migrate southwards in winter.

Scientific name	*Lanius excubitor*
Family	Laniidae
Size	23–25cm (9–10in) long
Distribution	Many parts of North America, Europe, Asia and North Africa
Habitat	Very varied, from woodland and scrub to marshland, tundra and desert
Diet	Insects; small birds, mammals, lizards and frogs
Breeding	Builds bulky nest of twigs, moss and grass in tree; up to seven blotched eggs (fewer in warm areas), incubated by female for 14–16 days

Red-backed shrike

This species, like the great grey shrike, often impales its prey – whether a large insect such as a grasshopper, beetle or dragonfly, or a small mammal or bird – on a thorn or barb, earning it the nickname 'butcher-bird'. Scientists believe that this habit arose because the bird had difficulty holding the prey in its claw while dismembering it. The thorn acted like a butcher's hook, and the bird would leave uneaten parts for later; this behaviour evolved into the habitual storage of prey in a hedgerow 'larder'. Interestingly, the red-backed shrike does not seem to store its prey in this way in Africa and south-western Asia, where it migrates for the winter.

Female

Male

Scientific name	*Lanius collurio*
Family	Laniidae
Size	16–18cm (6½–7in) long
Distribution	Much of Europe and western Asia; migrates southwards in winter
Habitat	Open woodlands; scrub; heaths; cultivated land
Diet	Insects; small vertebrates
Breeding	Grass-lined twiggy nest built in dense bush or hedge; four to seven eggs, incubated by female for about 14 days

Blue vanga shrike

Vanga shrikes, or vangas, are an isolated family of somewhat shrike-like birds that are confined to Madagascar and one nearby island. They may have evolved from helmet shrikes (an African group often put in a separate family from true shrikes, Prionopidae). Like other isolated groups (such as the Galápagos finches; *see p.270*), the vangas evolved rapidly to fill all available ecological niches. As a result, the birds vary widely, various species taking the places filled elsewhere by woodpeckers, nuthatches or tits, as well as true shrikes. The strikingly beautiful blue vanga lives in forest tree tops, searching for insects among the foliage, often in flocks of mixed species. A subspecies lives on Moheli island.

Scientific name	*Leptopterus madagascarinus*
Family	Vangidae
Size	About 15cm (6in) long
Distribution	Madagascar; Moheli (Comoro Islands)
Habitat	Upper layers of forests
Diet	Insects
Breeding	Details uncertain, but believed to build cup-shaped nest in tree;
	three or four eggs, probably incubated by both sexes (period unknown)

Bohemian waxwing

The name waxwing comes from the red drops of waxy material on the tips of the secondary wing feathers; their purpose is not known. The Bohemian waxwing is the most widely spread of the three species, and is often known simply as the waxwing in areas (such as Europe and most of Asia) where it is the only species. The others are the Cedar waxwing (*Bombycilla cedrorum*) of North and Central America and the Japanese waxwing (*B. japonica*). Waxwings are gregarious birds that migrate to the south of their range and winter in large flocks. They also breed together, each with only a small nest territory. Every few years, large numbers of waxwings spread well south of their normal wintering range.

Scientific name	*Bombycilla garrulus*
Family	Bombycillidae
Size	About 18cm (8in) long
Distribution	Northern North America, Europe and Asia, except Arctic
Habitat	Mainly conifer and birch forests; may spread to fields and gardens
Diet	Mainly berries and fruits; some insects
Breeding	Bulky nest of plant material hidden in foliage of tree; three to seven spotted eggs, incubated mainly by female for 12–16 days

Dipper

Dippers are the only truly aquatic members of the Passeriformes. They can wade, swim, dive and possibly even walk, completely submerged, on the river bottom. Their eyes function well in both air and water, and special flaps seal their nostrils to prevent water entering. A much larger than normal preen gland produces oil that keeps their feathers waterproof. The name dipper refers to their frequent 'bobbing' movements rather than to dipping into the water. The common dipper of Europe and Asia is also called the white-breasted dipper to distinguish it from the all-brown American dipper (*Cinclus mexicanus*), found in mountains from Alaska to Panama.

Scientific name	*Cinclus cinclus*
Family	Cinclidae
Size	About 18cm (7in) long
Distribution	Mainly upland parts of Europe, Asia and north-western Africa
Habitat	Fast-running streams in hilly and mountainous country
Diet	Mainly aquatic insect larvae; other invertebrates; small fish; tadpoles
Breeding	Large domed nest of moss and leaves in crevice or between roots, often behind waterfall; usually five eggs, incubated by female for 16–17 days

Common or winter wren

Few birds are regarded so fondly as the tiny wren (known in North America as the winter wren). This is due in part to its plump body with cocked tail, in part to its rather secretive but busy manner – it is often seen in gardens, but usually scurrying among the undergrowth – and in part to the the fact that it sings melodiously and very loudly for so small a bird. Its scientific name, like the French name *troglodyte*, means 'cave-dweller', and refers to its domed nest with side entrance, which is often hidden in a rock crevice. Males build several nests, lure females with courtship flights and singing, and mate with as many females as they can attract to a nest.

Scientific name	*Troglodytes troglodytes*
Family	Troglodytidae
Size	9–10cm (3½–4in) long
Distribution	Much of temperate Northern Hemisphere
Habitat	Varied: woodland; scrubland; fields; heaths; parks; gardens; sea cliffs
Diet	Mainly insects and their larvae; some berries
Breeding	Polygynous. Males build several dome-shaped nests of plant material; each female lays up to ten eggs and incubates them for 14–16 days

Cactus wren

The cactus wren contrasts in several ways with the common or winter wren (*see p.241*). It is much bigger, with a longer tail, and is bolder in its habits. It moves openly around its habitat, searching for food on the ground, in small family groups whose numbers give some protection from predators. It can run swiftly but also flies quite well, with whirring wings. It builds nests high up in large cacti, yuccas and other desert plants for roosting and shelter as well as breeding. Unlike the common wren, it is monogamous (has only one mate), and may produce four broods a year; the young help to feed their younger siblings and protect the family's territory.

Scientific name	*Campylorhynchus brunneicapillus*
Family	Troglodytidae
Size	18–22cm (7–8½in) long
Distribution	South-western United States; northern half of Mexico
Habitat	Desert; arid scrubland
Diet	Ground-living insects and other invertebrates; sometimes small lizards
Breeding	Dome-shaped nest of dry plant material, lined with feathers, on cactus or other plant; three to seven eggs, incubated by female for 16–17 days

Brown thrasher

Thrashers get their name from the way they flick – or 'thrash' – leaves as they forage in undergrowth and leaf litter of the forest floor for insects. They have long been thought to be related to both wrens and thrushes (the brown thrasher looks rather like a very large thrush, but behaves in a wren-like way), but recent DNA studies suggest that their closest relations may in fact be starlings (*see p.294*). The brown thrasher is a shy bird, and much bigger than other species living in its habitat. It sometimes sings – repeating each phrase twice – from an open perch, but usually sings from cover. Northern populations migrate southwards in winter.

Scientific name	*Toxostoma rufum*
Family	Mimidae
Size	28–30cm (11–12in) long
Distribution	Southern Canada and United States east of Rockies
Habitat	Thickets and forest edges
Diet	Mainly insects
Breeding	Cup-shaped, smoothly lined nest of plant material in bush or undergrowth; up to five eggs, incubated by female for 12–13 days

Common or northern mockingbird

One of the best-known American garden birds, the mockingbird is named and renowned for its ability to mimic the calls and songs of other creatures – mostly other birds, but also things as bizarre as frogs, pianos, whistles and squeaking wheels. It sings all year – day and sometimes night – usually from a prominent perch such as a fence post or telephone wire, repeating each phrase three or four times. Another factor in people's familiarity with the mockingbird is its fearlessness and strong territorial instinct; it will even defend its territory from a family cat or dog. It lives all year in the south, but northern populations migrate southwards in winter.

Scientific name	*Mimus polyglottos*
Family	Mimidae
Size	23–28cm (9–11in) long
Distribution	Southern Canada; most of USA and Mexico; parts of Caribbean
Habitat	Open woodland; open country with thickets; gardens; orchards
Diet	Insects and other small creatures; berries and fruits
Breeding	Nest a bulky open cup made of twigs and other material, on a low branch; up to five spotted eggs, incubated by female for 12–13 days

Dunnock, or hedge accentor

Commonly but incorrectly called the hedge sparrow, the dunnock has a slimmer, more pointed bill than true European sparrows (*see pp.291–292*) and has grey foreparts. It is slimmer, and lacks the black bib of the tree sparrow and male house sparrow and the brown head of the female house sparrow. Dunnocks are rather unobtrusive birds but are among the commonest songbirds of western Europe. They spend most of their time on the ground, searching for food, but fly briefly up to a perch to sing their warbling song. It is resident all year in Britain and much of western Europe, but northern and eastern populations migrate south in winter.

Scientific name	*Prunella modularis*
Family	Prunellidae
Size	14–15cm (5½–6in) long
Distribution	Most of Europe; parts of western Asia and Middle East
Habitat	Woodland; hedgerows; scrubland; parks; gardens; coasts
Diet	Insects and their larvae; fruits and seeds, especially in winter
Breeding	Neat cup-shaped nest of twigs, grass and moss, in bush or hedge; three to six eggs, incubated by female for about 12 days

Eastern bluebird

Not only does this bluebird have a colourful combination of bright blue, orange-red and white plumage, but it is also – like many members of the thrush family – a fine though relatively soft singer. The female has similar but slightly duller colouring. Two related species live in western North America: the western bluebird (*Sialia mexicana*), which has smaller red patches, and the mountain bluebird (*S. currucoides*), which has no red. Eastern bluebirds are often seen perching on fences or wires, but they feed mainly on the ground. Northern populations gather in large flocks before migrating south for the winter. Competition for nesting sites has reduced their numbers in recent decades.

Scientific name	*Sialia sialis*
Family	Turdidae; sometimes included in Muscicapidae
Size	16.5–19cm (6½–7½in) long
Distribution	Southern Canada to Nicaragua, east of Rockies
Habitat	Open woodland; farmland; orchards; parks; gardens
Diet	Insects; fruits and berries (especially in winter)
Breeding	Cup-shaped nest of plant materials in natural or old woodpecker hole in tree or stump; three to six eggs, incubated by female for 13–15 days

Black redstart

A widespread species with several subspecies that vary in their amounts of black and red plumage, the black redstart is always darker-looking than the closely related common redstart (*Phoenicurus phoenicurus*), which is red and grey, with a black face on the male. Black redstarts originally nested mainly on sea-cliffs and other rocky places, but have adapted well to urban life, nesting on buildings – often factories, dock buildings or power stations – and feeding on waste and rubble-strewn ground. They often perch on rocks or walls, singing rather hoarsely, and then, with a shake of the tail, pounce to catch insects on the ground or in the air.

Scientific name	*Phoenicurus ochruros*
Family	Turdidae; sometimes included in Muscicapidae
Size	14–15cm (5½–6in) long
Distribution	Parts of Europe; North and East Africa; parts of Asia (to India and China)
Habitat	Cliffs; open rocky areas; towns and cities; industrial areas and wasteland
Diet	Mainly insects and larvae; some berries
Breeding	Loose cup-shaped nest of plant materials on cliff or building, or in hollow; four to six glossy eggs, incubated by female for 12–14 days

Fieldfare

The combination of grey head and rump, chestnut back and speckled underparts with 'arrowhead' markings distinguishes the fieldfare from other birds of the large genus *Turdus*, the true thrushes. Fieldfares are fairly aggressive, noisy birds with a rather squeaky, babbling song. They are migrants, breeding in northern and central Europe and northern Asia, and flying to southern and western Europe and south-west Asia for the winter. In summer they frequent forests, woodland and wooded parks, and may even breed on the treeless tundra, nesting on buildings. In winter they often gather in large flocks with other thrushes to feed on grassy fields.

Scientific name	*Turdus pilaris*
Family	Turdidae; sometimes included in Muscicapidae
Size	About 25cm (10in) long
Distribution	Most of Europe and northern Asia; migrant (*see above*)
Habitat	Mainly woodland in breeding season; fields and grassland in winter
Diet	Worms, insects and other invertebrates; berries and fruits in winter
Breeding	Large cup-shaped nest of plant materials and mud, normally in tree or bush; usually three to five eggs, incubated by female for 13–15 days

Song thrush

The song thrush is a familiar and welcome inhabitant of parks and gardens in north-western Europe (and in New Zealand and parts of Australia, where it was introduced in the 1860s). Elsewhere, however, it is mainly a woodland bird. It is renowned for its melodious song, sung all year, in which each phrase is repeated twice or more. Its boldly speckled brown colouring distinguishes it from the larger, greyer mistle thrush (*Turdus viscivorus*). It is known for cocking its head to one side, apparently 'listening' for worms (but in fact looking), and for using a favourite 'anvil' stone to smash snails' shells. It may be threatened by the use of slug-killers.

Scientific name	*Turdus philomelos*
Family	Turdidae; sometimes included in Muscicapidae
Size	About 23cm (9in) long
Distribution	Europe; North Africa; western and central Asia; Australasia (introduced)
Habitat	Woodland; fields; parks; gardens
Diet	Invertebrates (especially snails and worms); berries and small fruits
Breeding	Cup-shaped nest of plant materials and mud, in tree or bush; usually three to five blue, spotted eggs, incubated by female for 13–14 days

American robin

The American robin, like several species around the world, was named because of its red breast, but it is a much bigger bird than the 'original', Eurasian robin (*opposite*). It is the only true thrush of the genus *Turdus* native to North America, and apart from its colouring is similar to the Eurasian blackbird (*Turdus merula*). American robins were originally woodland birds, but adapted well to human expansion and are among the most common and loved American garden birds. They have a sweet song, a sure sign of spring in many areas. At one time they were widely shot for sport and food, and were later threatened by the use of pesticides.

Scientific name	*Turdus migratorius*
Family	Turdidae; sometimes included in Muscicapidae
Size	About 25cm (10in) long
Distribution	North America except far north; winters in Gulf States to Guatemala
Habitat	Woodland and forest edges; parks; gardens
Diet	Berries and small fruits; insects; snails
Breeding	Cup-shaped nest of twigs, straw, grass and mud, in tree, bush or crevice; usually about four eggs, incubated mainly by female for 12–14 days

Eurasian robin

A familiar garden bird in Britain and some other parts of western Europe – where a robin will perch within a metre or two (a few feet) of a gardener, watching for unearthed worms or other snacks – this bird is much more shy over most other parts of its range. There, it is a retiring bird of deep woodland. Wherever they live, robins' friendliness does not extend to other robins. Both males and females guard their territory aggressively. They do so by singing their loud, plaintive, warbling song – with head raised and chest puffed out – virtually all year, except during the summer moult and the coldest winter weather (when finding food takes priority).

Scientific name	*Erithacus rubecula*
Family	Turdidae; sometimes included in Muscicapidae
Size	About 14cm (5½in) long
Distribution	Europe; western and south-western Asia; North Africa
Habitat	Woodland; hedgerows; parks; gardens
Diet	Ground-living insects and larvae; worms; snails; some berries
Breeding	Cup-shaped nest of plant material in bush, hedge, creeper, crevice, hole in tree ; five to seven spotted eggs, incubated by female for 12–14 days

Nightingale

Nightingales are shy, unobtrusive birds, far less often seen than heard. The most renowned singers in a highly tuneful family, they belie their name by singing just as frequently in the daytime as the evening and night. But the vigorous, widely varied stream of notes – ranging from harsh to liquid and flute-like – is certainly most striking late on a quiet, warm, late-spring evening. Males usually arrive from wintering grounds in tropical Africa and south-west Asia a week or two before the females, and establish breeding territories. As with most songbirds, the males sing to claim this territory, aiming to entice a female while keeping other males away.

Scientific name	*Luscinia megarhynchos*
Family	Turdidae; sometimes included in Muscicapidae
Size	16–17cm (6¼–6¾in) long
Distribution	Much of Europe; North Africa; south-west to central Asia; migratory
Habitat	Woodland; thickets; undergrowth; heathland
Diet	Worms; insects; larvae; berries
Breeding	Cup-shaped nest of plant materials on or near ground in undergrowth; four or five eggs, incubated by female for 13–14 days

White-crested laughing thrush

So called because of their loud, cackling calls, the laughing thrushes are generally grouped in a separate family of mostly Old World tropical birds, the babblers and wren-tits. However, genetic evidence suggests that they are closely related to Old World warblers (*see pp.254–255*), so some biologists place them in that family. The white-crested laughing thrush – one of about 55 Asian species – has a striking white crest, a white breast and black facial markings. These contrast with the rest of the body's brown plumage, whose shade varies among the several geographical races. It is a sociable bird, moving through the forest in small flocks, foraging on the ground and among undergrowth for food.

Scientific name	*Garrulax leucolophus*
Family	Timaliidae; sometimes included in Muscicapidae or Sylviidae
Size	About 30cm (12in) long
Distribution	Himalayas east to south-west China; south-east Asia; Sumatra
Habitat	Forest
Diet	Insects; seeds; berries; sometimes nectar, lizards
Breeding	Cup-shaped nest of grass, bamboo leaves and other plant material in bush or low tree; three to six eggs, incubated by both sexes for 14 days

Marsh warbler

Old World warblers – which are completely unrelated to the New World group of the same name (*see p.277*) – include a number of very similar species that are often more easily distinguished by their song than their appearance. In particular, the marsh warbler and reed warbler (*Acrocephalus scirpaceus*) have only minor differences of colouring. Both live in or near marshland, but the reed warbler is more likely to be found deep in reedbeds while the marsh warbler lives in thickets nearby. Its song is much more tuneful – often mimicking other birds – than the harsh song of the reed warbler. Both build intricate nests among the plant stems.

Scientific name	*Acrocephalus scirpaceus*
Family	Sylviidae; sometimes included in Muscicapidae
Size	About 12.5cm (5in) long
Distribution	Much of Europe; parts of North Africa and south-western Asia
Habitat	Mainly beds of rushes, willows, etc., near water, rather than reedbeds
Diet	Marshland insects; berries
Breeding	Shallow cup-shaped nest, mainly of grass, attached to plant stems by 'handles'; four or five eggs, incubated by both sexes for about 12 days

Blackcap

Sometimes known as the 'northern nightingale', the blackcap has a beautiful, powerful warbling song which the male delivers from a perch hidden among deep undergrowth in his breeding territory. The song includes many phrases that mimic other birds' songs, but it ends abruptly. The bird's coloured cap – black in males, rusty-brown in females – makes the blackcap look much more distinctive than other warblers. (However, the male orphean warbler [*Sylvia hortensis*] of the Mediterranean area also has a black head.) Blackcaps migrate over long distances to wintering grounds in south-western Europe, the Middle East and tropical Africa.

Scientific name	*Sylvia atricapilla*
Family	Sylviidae; sometimes included in Muscicapidae
Size	13–15cm (5–6in) long
Distribution	Europe to central Asia, Middle East and North Africa; winters to south
Habitat	Woodland; heathland; gardens with thick undergrowth
Diet	Insects and larvae; small fruits and berries in autumn
Breeding	Frail nest of grass and other materials in bush, attached to stems by 'handles'; four or five eggs, incubated by both sexes for about 12 days

Variegated wren

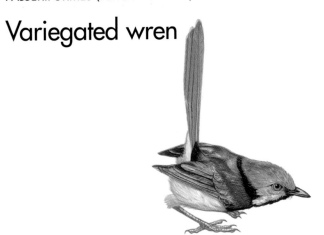

The mostly highly coloured 'wrens' of Australia and New Guinea are not related to true wrens (*see pp.241–242*), but got their name because they are small birds with a long upturned tail. They are more correctly known as fairy-wrens or wren-warblers. The variegated wren is a very variable species with several subspecies – whose males look rather similar but whose females are distinctive – seen in various parts of Australia. Their habitat varies from the arid interior (*Malurus lamberti assimilis*) and the Kimberleys (*M.l. rogersi*) to tropical Arnhem Land (*M.l. dulcis*) and the moist central eastern slopes of the Great Dividing Range (*M.l. lamberti*).

Scientific name	*Malurus lamberti*
Family	Maluridae; sometimes included in Muscicapidae
Size	About 14cm (5½in) long, including extended tail
Distribution	Most of Australia
Habitat	Various subspecies range from rainforest to arid habitats
Diet	Mainly insects
Breeding	Breeds at various seasons. Oval nest of plant material, near ground in bush or tussock; three or four speckled eggs, incubated for 12–15 days

Pied flycatcher

Old World flycatchers (of Europe, Asia, Africa and Australasia) are unrelated to the New World tyrant flycatchers (*see pp.215–216*), but they catch their food in the same manner. The bird perches – often on a tree branch – watching for a passing insect; then it dashes out to snatch its prey in mid-air. The pied flycatcher is one of three very similar summer visitors to Europe, but is the only one commonly seen in Britain. The others are the collared flycatcher (*Ficedula albicollis*), seen eastwards from France and Italy, and the semi-collared flycatcher (*F. semitorquata*) in south-east Europe. In each the male is black and white, the female brownish and white.

Scientific name	*Ficedula hypoleuca*
Family	Muscicapidae
Size	About 12.5cm (5in) long
Distribution	Most of Europe; parts of western Asia; winters in Middle East and Africa
Habitat	Woodland; orchards; gardens
Diet	Mainly flying insects
Breeding	Cup-shaped nest of moss and other plant materials in hollow tree or other cavity; two to six eggs, incubated by both sexes for 12–14 days

Golden whistler

Whistlers are named for their clear, melodious whistling song. That of the golden whistler and the mangrove golden whistler (*Pachycephala melanura*) of Australia's northern coast ends with a whip-crack sound. Only adult male golden whistlers have the beautiful olive-green, black (or grey) and yellow colouring shown; females are a duller olive-brown to olive-grey, with greyish or whitish underparts. However, there are 70 to 80 geographical races and subspecies – more than in any other bird species, and including 14 forms in Australia alone – with considerable colour variations. The birds move slowly and deliberately from branch to branch, searching the leaves and bark for insects and berries to eat.

Scientific name	*Pachycephala pectoralis*
Family	Pachycephalidae; sometimes included in Muscicapidae
Size	About 17cm (6½in) long
Distribution	Eastern, south-eastern and western Australia; Indonesia to Fiji
Habitat	Forest; woodland; mallee (eucalypt) scrub
Diet	Insects and larvae; berries
Breeding	Small cup-shaped nest of plant materials, in tall shrub or fork of tree; two or three eggs, incubated by both parents for about 17 days

Great tit

Tits, or titmice – including some species known in North America as chickadees – are small, active and acrobatic woodland birds that are common and popular garden species. They are unafraid, feed readily at bird tables – or hang upside-down to peck at hanging food – and often nest in nesting boxes. They vary in size and colouring, but are almost all instantly recognizable as members of the same family. The great tit is one of the largest, boldest and most widespread species, occurring from Morocco to Japan, Norway to Indonesia. Not surpisingly for such a widespread species, its blue, yellow and green plumage varies considerably over its range.

Scientific name	*Parus major*
Family	Paridae
Size	About 14cm (5½in) long
Distribution	Europe; north-west Africa; much of Asia except far north
Habitat	Forest; woodland; fields; hedges; parks; gardens
Diet	Insects, snails and other invertebrates; seeds, fruits, nuts and buds
Breeding	Cup-shaped nest of moss and grass in hole in tree or wall, or in nesting box; up to 12 eggs, incubated by female for 13–14 days

Black-capped chickadee

The name of this small, acrobatic bird comes from its 'chick-a-dee-dee-dee' call. It is as tame and friendly as most other members of the tit family, and is a common garden visitor in northern North America. It is constantly active, hopping from twig to twig in search of food. It is particularly tempted by sunflower seeds, peanuts or suet placed on a bird-table or feeder, or by a ball of fat and seeds hung from a tree branch. Both members of a pair have a strong instinct for excavating a nesting hole, usually making a new cavity even if last year's is empty nearby. For this reason, they will rarely use a nesting box unless it contains wood chips for them to 'excavate'.

Scientific name	*Parus atricapillus*
Family	Paridae
Size	About 14cm (5½in) long
Distribution	Eastern Alaska; southern Canada; northern parts of United States
Habitat	Coniferous forest; open woodland; thickets; gardens
Diet	Insects and larvae; snails; seeds; berries
Breeding	Nests in cavity dug in soft, rotting timber (rarely re-used), lined with moss and feathers; up to ten eggs, incubated by female for 11–13 days

Long-tailed tit

One of Europe's smallest birds by body volume, the long-tailed tit looks rather like a small fluffy ball of wool with a long tail – half its total length or more – attached. It is related to other tits, but is so distinct that (with seven other species) it is placed in a separate family. It is highly active, constantly searching trees and undergrowth for food or working in pairs to build their beautifully finished domed, oval nest. Long-tailed tits' tiny size means that they quickly lose body heat, so they shelter in woods in winter and roost huddled together in groups; even so, many die in severe weather. Their colouring varies widely over their geographical range.

Scientific name	*Aegithalos caudatus*
Family	Aegithalidae; formerly included in Paridae
Size	12.5–14cm (5–5½in) long, including tail
Distribution	Western Europe to Japan, north of Himalayas
Habitat	Open woodland; heaths; scrubland; hedges; parks
Diet	Mainly small insects and spiders; some seeds and buds
Breeding	Elaborate domed, feather-lined nest covered with lichen, in tree or bush; up to 12 freckled eggs, incubated mainly by female for 16 days

PASSERIFORMES (PERCHING BIRDS)

Velvet-fronted nuthatch

The name nuthatch refers to the fondness of European species – especially the Eurasian nuthatch (*Sitta europea*) – for acorns and hazel nuts. They store these in a bark crevice and 'hack' them open with their bill; 'nuthatch' is a corruption of 'nuthack'. However, the velvet-fronted and many other species live mainly or entirely on insects and other invertebrates. All nuthatches are stocky, short-necked little birds. They are extremely agile, climbing both up and headfirst down the trunk of trees and along branches in search of their food; no other bird is so nimble in climbing around a tree. Most nuthatches have a blue-grey back, but the velvet-fronted and the azure nuthatch (*S. azurea*) are both bright blue.

Scientific name	*Sitta frontalis*
Family	Sittidae
Size	About 12.5cm (5in) long
Distribution	Southern and south-eastern Asia, from India to Philippines
Habitat	Forests
Diet	Mainly insects and spiders
Breeding	Nests in natural hole in tree, lined with moss and grass; probably about four to seven eggs, incubated by female for 15–18 days

Treecreeper or brown creeper

Ornithologists disagree about how many distinct species of treecreepers – all small, grey-brown, well-camouflaged birds – there are. Many believe that the brown creeper or American treecreeper (*Certhia americana*), and perhaps also the short-toed treecreeper (*C. brachydactyla*) of southern and central Europe, are simply subspecies of the common Eurasian treecreeper (*C. familiaris*). In any case, the three species or subspecies are very difficult for non-experts to tell apart, differing mainly in minor variations of colour and pattern. They climb tree-trunks – unlike nuthatches always upwards, with head up – searching for bark insects and larvae, which they extract with their curving bill.

Scientific names	*Certhia familiaris; C. brachydactyla; C. americana*
Family	Certhiidae
Size	12–13cm (about 5in) long
Distribution	Europe; temperate Asia; temperate North America; Central America
Habitat	Woodland; parks
Diet	Mainly insects and larvae; some seeds and nuts
Breeding	Elongated cup-shaped nest of plant material in split in tree or behind loose bark or ivy; usually five or six eggs, incubated for 13–15 days

Purple-throated or van Hasselt's sunbird

Sunbirds are the Old World equivalents of the hummingbirds of the Americas (*see pp.174–179*), although the two groups are completely unrelated. Sunbirds are tiny birds that can hover briefly, but they are nowhere near such agile fliers as the hummingbirds. Instead, they usually cling to a forest flower with their strong claws while using their long curved bill to suck nectar. Most species are brilliantly coloured, but the male purple-throated sunbird is distinguished by its vivid amethyst throat, red belly, green head, and blue and black back; the female has an olive-green back and yellow belly. The female mainly builds the purse-shaped nest.

Scientific name	*Nectarinia* (or *Leptocoma*) *sperata*
Family	Nectariniidae
Size	About 10cm (4in) long
Distribution	Asia from Assam and Bangladesh to Vietnam, Indonesia and Philippines
Habitat	Open forest; scrubland; mangroves; gardens
Diet	Nectar; some small insects
Breeding	Oval nest of plant fibres, suspended from tree branch or palm frond; usually two eggs, incubated by female for 13–14 days

Eastern double-collared sunbird

Well over half of all sunbird species – which total more than 110 types of birds –
inhabit Africa south of the Sahara. Like their close cousins in southern Asia
(and a few species in Australia and the Pacific), they feed mainly on nectar, plus a
few small insects, which they take mainly while clambering over flowers. They
usually suck nectar by inserting their long, curved bill into a tubular flower (and
many flowers depend on sunbirds for pollination), but some shorter-billed sunbirds
pierce the base of a flower to reach its nectar. The eastern double-collared sunbird
is one of several African species with two colourful bands of feathers on the breast.

Scientific name	*Nectarinia* (or *Cinnyris*) *mediocris*
Family	Nectariniidae
Size	About 11cm (4½) long
Distribution	East Africa, from Congo and Kenya to Zambia and Mozambique
Habitat	Upland forests; bamboo thickets; scrubland; grassland; gardens
Diet	Nectar; small insects
Breeding	Domed nest of grass and other plant materials, in tree or bush; usually two eggs, incubated by female for 13–15 days

Tui

Nicknamed the parson bird because the tufts of white feathers at its throat look like a clergyman's bands, the tui is one of New Zealand's most renowned songbirds. It sings from a perch high in a tree, often from before dawn until after dusk, and even through moonlit nights. It is a member of the honeyeater family, whose members have a bristle-tipped tongue, like a paintbrush, which they use to extract flower nectar and fruit pulp. Nectar is tuis' favourite food, and they may travel long distances to get it. In the breeding season, male and female tuis chase each other around the nesting area, and sing duets. The male chases away any intruding males, and makes almost vertical display dives.

Scientific name	*Prosthemadera novaeseelandiae*
Family	Meliphagidae
Size	About 30cm (12in) long
Distribution	New Zealand and its offshore islands
Habitat	Forests; woodland; gardens
Diet	Nectar; fruits; large insects and other invertebrates
Breeding	Bulky, leaf-lined nest of twigs and sticks, usually high in tree; usually three or four blotched eggs, incubated by female for about 14 days

Noisy friarbird

The bare black skin on its head earned this bird the name leatherhead. It is also identified by its heavy, curved bill with an upright knob on the upper mandible (responsible for it being called 'knobby-nose'). It is an aggressive bird whose loud, raucous calls – especially vocal when it feeds in squabbling groups on flowering trees or orchard fruits – make the term 'noisy' very apt. Farmers have shot many noisy friarbirds because of their fondness for fruits such as grapes and pears. However, they also feed on harmful insects such as grasshoppers and beetles, as well as berries and the nectar of tubular flowers such as waratahs and grevilleas.

Scientific name	*Philemon corniculatus*
Family	Meliphagidae
Size	30–36cm (12–14in) long
Distribution	Eastern Australia; south-east New Guinea
Habitat	Sclerophyll (hard-leaved) forest; open woodland; orchards; farmland
Diet	Fruits; berries; nectar; pollen; insects
Breeding	Large, deep cup-shaped nest of stringy bark, grasses and wiry stems, in tree; usually two or three eggs, incubated for about 14–17 days

Black-headed bunting

Buntings are small, mainly seed-eating birds with a stout, conical bill well suited to crushing and dehusking seeds of grasses, grains and other plants. Members of the family living in North America – where the whole family is believed to have originated – are commonly called sparrows, but they are not closely related to the true Old World sparrows (*see pp.291–292*). Most buntings are rather dull-coloured, often streaked birds, but the black-headed bunting is an exception. However, only the male has the black head, bright yellow belly and chestnut-brown back illustrated; the female has paler yellow underparts and a buff and brown back.

Scientific name	*Emberiza melanocephala*
Family	Emberizidae; sometimes included in Fringillidae
Size	16–17cm (about 6½in) long
Distribution	South-eastern Europe; winters south-western Asia to India
Habitat	Open wooded and bushy country; olive groves; gardens
Diet	Mainly seeds (especially grains; some berries); some insects
Breeding	Cup-shaped nest of grass and other plant fibres, well hidden in low bush; usually three to six eggs, incubated by female for 14–16 days

Snow bunting

The striking white and black plumage of the snow bunting is the male's breeding-season colouring. At other times, the white areas become mottled with rusty-brown, and the black wing feathers become mostly brown. At all seasons the female is less striking, with a brownish back and buff markings on the head. However, both sexes, at any season, show a flash of white wing feathers as they fly. They are hardy little birds, breeding on the cold arctic and subarctic tundra and mountains. Males make display flights, when they hover in the air rather like skylarks (*see p.228*). Snow buntings winter in large flocks on rough open country, often near coasts.

Scientific name	*Plectrophenax nivalis*
Family	Emberizidae; sometimes included in Fringillidae
Size	16–17cm (about 6½in) long
Distribution	Northern Europe, Asia and North America
Habitat	Tundra and mountains; migrates S in winter to coasts and open country
Diet	Mainly seeds; insects in summer
Breeding	Nest of grass, moss and lichen, among stones; four to six eggs, incubated by female for 10–15 days

Darwin's medium ground finch

When the naturalist Charles Darwin visited the Galápagos Islands, in the Pacific, in 1835, he realized that the 13 species of 'finches' (actually members of the bunting family) living there were a living demonstration of the process of evolution. Darwin suggested – and DNA evidence has since confirmed – that they all evolved in isolation from a common ancestor species that reached the Galápagos from South America at least a million years ago. Each species, plus another on the nearby Cocos Islands, has a different-shaped bill, adapted to a certain diet and habitat. Three species of ground finches have a seed-crushing bill, and often feed in mixed flocks.

Scientific name	*Geospiza fortis*
Family	Emberizidae; sometimes put in Cardinalidae or included in Fringillidae
Size	About 13cm (5in) long
Distribution	Galápagos Islands
Habitat	Arid and semi-arid scrubland
Diet	Mainly seeds; some ticks and other insects; reptiles' eggs
Breeding	Male builds several dome-shaped nests of plant materials; female choses nest and incubates usually two to four eggs for about 12 days

Red-crested cardinal

Despite its name, this species is not very closely related to the true cardinals (*see pp.272–274*). It has an attractive combination of grey and white plumage, with a striking scarlet head, crest and chin. It is a lively bird, with a bold manner, and also has a rich, melodious voice. Not surprisingly, it is kept as a caged bird by some people, especially in its native South America; it breeds readily in captivity. Red-crested cardinals have also been successfully introduced elsewhere – notably in Hawaii. They have the typical long legs of a ground-feeding bird, and are often seen in pairs, groups or small flocks – especially near waterways – feeding on seeds.

Scientific name	*Paroaria coronata*
Family	Emberizidae; sometimes included in Fringillidae
Size	About 19cm (7½in) long
Distribution	South America from Bolivia and southern Brazil to northern Argentina
Habitat	Grassland with scattered bushes and trees
Diet	Seeds
Breeding	Cup-shaped nest of grass and other plant materials in bush or small tree; two to five eggs, incubated for 12–13 days

Pyrrhuloxia

Pyrrhuloxias are much greyer in colouring than the closely related common or northern cardinal (*opposite*), but males do have beautiful red markings on the breast, face, crest and wings. Females are greyish-brown, with little red, and except for their yellow bill look much like female northern cardinals. Pyrrhuloxias have a strong bill that is ideal for crushing mesquite seeds, but they also eat insects – including the cotton worms and weevils that attack cotton crops. They often hide in dense mesquite thickets, but may be seen feeding in flocks of up to a thousand birds in winter. In the breeding season, males defend their territory and feed their mate during courtship and incubation of the eggs.

Scientific name	*Cardinalis sinuatus* or *Pyrrhuloxia sinuata*
Family	Emberizidae or Cardinalidae; sometimes included in Fringillidae
Size	19–22cm (7½–8¾in) long
Distribution	South-western United States; northern Mexico
Habitat	Desert scrub, mesquite thickets and dry creek beds; semi-arid grassland
Diet	Mainly seeds; also cactus fruits and insects
Breeding	Small nest of twigs and other plant materials in mesquite or on ground
	at base; two to four eggs, incubated by female for about 14 days

Common or northern cardinal

The brilliant red male cardinal is unmistakable, but the female is a much duller brownish colour, with reddish-tinged wings and crest. Their name comes from the similarity to a Catholic Church cardinal's robes. Both sexes have a bright red bill, and both also sing their loud, clear, musical and richly varied songs almost all year round. Cardinals mostly live and search for their food in thickets and undergrowth, but they are common visitors to back yards in most of eastern and southern North America. They are many people's favourite birds, and have been adopted as the state bird of seven US states. Their range is still extending, despite their nests being parasitized by the brown-headed cowbird (*Molothrus ater*).

Scientific name	*Cardinalis cardinalis*
Family	Emberizidae or Cardinalidae; sometimes included in Fringillidae
Size	20–23cm (8–9in) long
Distribution	South-eastern Canada; eastern and southern USA; Mexico; Guatemala
Habitat	Woodland edges; thickets; parks; gardens
Diet	Mainly seeds and berries; also insects
Breeding	Mates for life. Rough cup-shaped nest of twigs and leaves, in foliage of bush or tree; three or four eggs, incubated by female for 12–13 days

Painted bunting

With colouring reminiscent of a parrot or other bird of tropical rainforests, the male painted bunting is probably the most colourful bird of North America. But as with most buntings and cardinals, the female is much duller, with a greenish back and greenish-yellow underparts. Nor is even the colourful male often seen, since the birds are very shy and prefer to stay in deep undergrowth. The best time to spot one is at dawn in the breeding season, when males – which have a strong territorial instinct – sing briefly from the top of the bush in which they live. Painted buntings are mainly seed-eaters, but need fresh small insects to feed to their young.

Scientific name	*Passerina ciris*
Family	Emberizidae or Cardinalidae; sometimes included in Fringillidae
Size	13–14cm (5–5½in) long
Distribution	Southern and south-eastern USA; Mexico; winters Gulf states to Panama
Habitat	Woodland edges; thickets near streams; garden undergrowth
Diet	Seeds, especially of grasses; some insects and larvae
Breeding	Deep cup-shaped nest of twigs and grass in shrub or small tree; usually three or four eggs, incubated by female for 11–12 days

Crimson-collared tanager

The name tanager is an English version of 'tangara', the name given to this large family of birds by the Tupi people of the Amazon basin. There are more than 230 species, living in the Americas from Canada to Chile and Argentina, including a number in the Caribbean, but by far the majority inhabit the tropics and subtropics of Central and South America. The crimson-collared tanager is typically colourful, with the female little different from the male. (Some other species have brilliant yellow, blue or green feathers, but some females are a dull brown.) It is a forest bird that feeds among the foliage in pairs, small groups or sometimes mixed flocks.

Scientific name	*Ramphocelus sanguinolentus*
Family	Emberizidae or Thraupidae; sometimes included in Fringillidae
Size	About 18cm (7in) long
Distribution	Central America, mainly east of mountains, from Mexico to Panama
Habitat	Mainly rainforest, woodland and forest edges, to 1100m (3600ft)
Diet	Fruits; insects
Breeding	Compact cup-shaped nest of leaves, mosses and other plant material in tree; usually two pale blue, spotted eggs, incubated for about 14 days

Swallow-tanager

The swallow-tanager differs from other tanagers in several ways, and it was once placed in a family of its own, Tersinidae. Today it is thought – backed up by DNA evidence – to be simply an 'oddball' member of the tanager family (Thraupidae), which is itself often included in the bunting family (Emberizidae) or even in a still bigger family (Fringillidae) that includes the finches. Unlike other tanagers, it has a broad, flat bill, which it uses to remove and eat the outer pulp from fruits before dropping the seed. It also 'hawks' to catch insects on the wing. It is the only hole-nesting tanager, and migrates from the lowlands up to higher altitudes to breed.

Scientific name	*Tersina viridis*
Family	Emberizidae or Thraupidae; sometimes included in Fringillidae
Size	About 15cm (6in) long
Distribution	Eastern Panama to northern Argentina and southern Brazil
Habitat	Forests and woodland; clearings; parks
Diet	Fruits; insects
Breeding	Nests in hole in tree or wall, or in tunnel dug in earth bank; usually three glossy eggs, incubated by female for 13–17 days

Magnolia warbler

The magnolia warbler is not well named. Firstly, although it sings pleasantly, it does not – in common with most members of the New World warbler or wood-warbler family – have a warbling, trilling song like that of the unrelated Old World warblers (*see pp.254–255*). Nor does it usually frequent magnolia trees – although the first bird described by an ornithologist about 1810 was found in such a tree. In its northern breeding grounds it mainly lives among conifers, but during spring and autumn migrations it is often seen in most of eastern North America, and sometimes in the West Indies. The female is duller, with less distinct markings, than the male.

Scientific name	*Dendroica magnoliae*
Family	Parulidae; sometimes included in Emberizidae or Fringillidae
Size	About 13cm (5in) long
Distribution	Breeds in Canada and north-eastern USA; winters Mexico to Panama
Habitat	Moist coniferous and mixed forest; winters in lowlands and forest edges
Diet	Mainly insects and spiders from leaves and bark; a few berries
Breeding	Well-built nest of fine twigs, stems and other plant materials, in conifer; three to five eggs, incubated by female for 11–13 days

Spot-breasted oriole

T he word 'icter' is Latin for yellow, and many members of this family – and
particularly the so-called orioles (which are not related to the Old World orioles;
see p.296) – have beautiful bright yellow or orange feathers, often combined with
black. In fact many other members of the family are all or predominantly black,
including the American blackbirds (which again are unrelated to their Old World
namesake). Ornithologists call the entire family the icterids. Male and female spot-
breasted orioles have distinctive black spotting on their breast, unlike any related
species. Like other orioles and close relatives, they weave an intricate hanging nest.

Scientific name	*Icterus pectoralis*
Family	Icteridae; sometimes included in Emberizidae or Fringillidae
Size	About 22cm (8½in) long
Distribution	Mexico to Costa Rica; south-eastern Florida (probably introduced)
Habitat	Open woodland; clearings; forest edges; parks; gardens
Diet	Leaf-living insects; nectar
Breeding	Intricately woven purse-shaped nest of grass and plant fibres, hanging
	from branch of tall tree; two to five eggs, incubated for 12–15 days

278

Iiwi, or Hawaiian honeycreeper

The Hawaiian honeycreepers show just as vivid an example of rapid evolution in an isolated environment as Darwin's finches (*see p.270*). They are a very diverse group of about 40 known types (many now extinct) that were once thought to make up a distinct family. There are parrot-like species, ones with a seed-crushing bill, slim ones that resemble warblers, and ones (like the iiwi – named by Hawaiians after its call) with a slender down-curved bill for sucking nectar. All evolved from an ancestor that reached Hawaii less than 5 million years ago. DNA studies show it to have been a finch, so ornithologists now often include them in the finch family.

Scientific name	*Vestiaria coccinea*
Family	Drepanadidae; often now included in Fringillidae
Size	About 15cm (6in) long
Distribution	Hawaii
Habitat	Wet upland forests and shrubland
Diet	Mainly nectar of flowering trees
Breeding	Loose cup-shaped nest of twigs and other plant material, high in canopy of tree; two to four spotted eggs, incubated for 13–14 days

Chaffinch

Chaffinches are common woodland birds in most of Europe, western Asia and the Mediterranean region, and have readily taken to living in gardens. Females lack the distinctive pink breast and grey crown of the male, and are a duller, brownish colour with a creamy breast. Chaffinches have a pleasant song, with many regional 'dialects'. They fly in typically undulating finch fashion. In winter, they form large flocks, often with the rather similar but more orange-breasted brambling (*Fringilla montifringilla*) to feed on fields or, in the case of northern and eastern populations, to migrate to less cold parts; some Asian chaffinches reach as far south as India.

Scientific name	*Fringilla coelebs*
Family	Fringillidae
Size	About 15cm (6in) long
Distribution	Eurasia to western Siberia; North Africa; Middle East; some migrate
Habitat	Forest; woodland; fields; hedges; gardens
Diet	Mainly seeds (including grains) and fruits; some insects and worms
Breeding	Neat, cup-shaped mossy nest in fork of tree or bush; usually four or five eggs, incubated by female for 11–13 days

Eurasian goldfinch

This beautiful, colourful finch was once widely caught and kept as a caged bird, and it became endangered in Britain in the late 19th century. It was saved by one of the first bird-conservation campaigns. Its sharply-pointed bill is well adapted to prising the deep-seated seeds from thistle and teasel heads, and for this reason goldfinches often feed in small flocks or family groups (known as 'charms' of goldfinches) on waste ground where such weeds grow. The male's courtship display involves showing the bright yellow wing bars. In the related American goldfinch (*Carduelis tristis*), the male's breeding plumage is almost all yellow, with black.

Scientific name	*Carduelis carduelis*
Family	Fringillidae
Size	About 12cm (4¾in) long
Distribution	Western Europe and North Africa to south-west and central Asia
Habitat	Farmland; woodland; gardens; wasteland (especially in winter)
Diet	Seeds (especially thistles, teasels and other weeds); young fed on insects
Breeding	Neat nest of plant materials, lined with wool and down, usually on
	tree branch; usually five or six eggs, incubated by female for 12–13 days

Common or red crossbill

The finches vary widely in bill shape to suit a particular diet. In the crossbills the tips of the two mandibles cross over, enabling the birds to prise open pine and other conifer cones to get at the seeds. These seeds are almost their only food, with occasional wild fruits and insects. When feeding, crossbills often shuffle sideways along a branch, parrot-fashion, or even hang upside-down to reach a cone. There are several very similar species, with overlapping territories. The two-barred, or white-winged, crossbill (*Loxia leucoptera*) of north-eastern Europe, Asia and North America has prominent white wing-bars. In all species, the female is greenish.

Scientific name	*Loxia curvirostra*
Family	Fringillidae
Size	About 16.5cm (6½in) long
Distribution	Much of Europe, Asia, North and Central America, in suitable habitat
Habitat	Coniferous forests
Diet	Almost solely conifer seeds
Breeding	Substantial nest of twigs lined with grass, in conifer; three or four greenish eggs, incubated by female for 13–16 days

Eurasian bullfinch

With its colourful plumage (a much duller pink in females), black cap and portly, thickset appearance, the bullfinch is easily recognized. In spite of its handsome appearance and quiet warbling song, it is unpopular with many gardeners and fruit-farmers because it is partial to the plump spring flower and fruit buds of ornamental shrubs and orchard trees. It does considerable damage to unprotected fruit crops, but it also eats many types of seeds (including those of weeds) and berries. It is rather a shy bird, keeping to deep woodland in many areas, and even in gardens (where it often feeds in pairs) quickly hides from humans.

Scientific name	*Pyrrhula pyrrhula*
Family	Fringillidae
Size	About 16cm (6¼in) long
Distribution	Most of Europe and Asia north of Himalayas, except far north, to Japan
Habitat	Coniferous forest; woodland; farmland; orchards; parks; gardens
Diet	Buds in spring; berries and seeds at other times
Breeding	May mate for life. Shallow cup-shaped nest of twigs and moss, in thick bush or hedge; four or five eggs, incubated by female for 12–14 days

Pine grosbeak

One of the biggest finches, the male pine grosbeak is a distinctive carmine-pink colour, while the female is yellowish-brown or greenish; both sexes have white wing-bars, a grey rump and a longer tail than most of their relatives. As their name suggests, pine grosbeaks have a large bill (although not as big as that of some other birds called grosbeaks), with which they eat buds, shoots, berries (such as rowan berries and blueberries) and other plant foods. They are normally resident in their northern forest habitat all year, but in some years – whether due to harsh weather or an increase in numbers – they spread in flocks much farther south than normal.

Scientific name	*Pinicola enucleator*
Family	Fringillidae
Size	20–22cm (8–9in) long
Distribution	Northern Europe, Asia and North America, except far north
Habitat	Coniferous and mixed forest, especially with fruiting undergrowth
Diet	Buds; shoots; berries; seeds; insects in summer
Breeding	Cup-shaped nest of twigs, moss and other plant materials, in pine or birch tree; usually four eggs, incubated by female for 13–14 days

Red avadavat

Waxbills – so called because of their glossy mandibles – and their relatives the grass-finches are gregarious, seed-eating birds, very similar to true finches, that are found mainly in tropical Africa, Asia and Australasia. The red avadavat – the name is a corruption of Ahmadabad, in India, from where the first specimens in Europe came – is a tiny waxbill that lives in huge flocks in wetlands and long grass. The male has brilliant red breeding plumage. It is a popular caged bird that is very tame in captivity. Escaped and deliberately introduced specimens have established themselves in a number of places, including parts of Portugal and southern Spain.

Scientific name	*Amandava* (or *Estrilda*) *amandava*
Family	Estrildidae; sometimes included in Ploceidae or Passeridae
Size	9–10cm (3½–4in) long
Distribution	Southern Asia from Pakistan to south-west China and Indonesia
Habitat	Scrub, grassland and fields, usually near water; reedbeds
Diet	Mainly grass seeds
Breeding	Breeds irregularly, most often in rainy season. Ball-shaped nest of grass with side entrance; six to ten eggs, incubated by female for 10–14 days

## PASSERIFORMES (PERCHING BIRDS)

Zebra finch

This tiny, lively, highly gregarious and beautifully patterned finch is named after the black and white bars on its tail. It is known far beyond its native habitat, because it is a favourite caged bird and is also widely used in laboratories for the investigation of bird behaviour and inheritance. In Australia it is the most common and widespread member of the grass-finch family. Zebra finches are often seen in large flocks moving as one between bushes, trees and the ground as they feed. They fly long distances in search of food and water, and Aboriginals and early European explorers in central Australia often found life-saving water by following the birds.

Scientific name	*Poephila guttata*
Family	Estrildidae; sometimes included in Ploceidae or Passeridae
Size	9–10cm (3½–4in) long
Distribution	Most of Australia; south-eastern Indonesia
Habitat	Most habitats in range, except wet coastal forests, including desert
Diet	Mainly grass seeds; a few insects
Breeding	Pairs for life; may breed at any season. Flask-shaped nest of grass stems in bush or low tree; four to six eggs, incubated by both sexes for 12 days

Long-tailed grass-finch

The long-tailed finch is a highly social species. Pairs bond for life, and are rarely separated by more than a metre or two (a few feet) on the ground or in the air. They form loose flocks of 10 to 15 pairs to feed on seeds that have fallen to the ground, or may pull down plants' seed-heads to reach their food. They drink by sucking water from pools, or even sucking up single drops of dew from blades of grass; they are said to be able to catch drops of falling rain. Whenever a member of a flock lands, they go through a head-bobbing ritual of recognition that is unique among finches. Head-bobbing is also part of their courtship ritual. Pairs strengthen the bond between them by mutual preening, and share nest-building.

Scientific name	*Poephila acuticauda*
Family	Estrildidae; sometimes included in Ploceidae or Passeridae
Size	About 15cm (6in) long
Distribution	Northern Australia
Habitat	Dry savannah grassland, especially among eucalypts by creeks or rivers
Diet	Mainly seeds; some flying insects and larvae
Breeding	Mates for life. Flask-shaped nest of woven grass stems with entrance tunnel; four or five eggs, incubated by both sexes for 10–14 days

Paradise whydah

Male

Female

The whydahs (or whidahs, named after the West African town of Ouidah) are an example of how difficult it is to classify the finches and their allies. Some ornithologists group them with waxbills (family Estrildidae), some with weavers (Ploceidae), while some group all these in the family Passeridae, with the sparrows. Like other whydahs (sometimes called widows), the male paradise whydah grows tail feathers twice as long as the rest of his body during the breeding season. He makes elaborate display flights, the tail feathers held out almost at a right angle, to court a female. After they mate, she lays her eggs in another bird's nest, cuckoo-fashion, while the male courts and mates with another female.

Scientific name	*Vidua* (or *Steganura*) *paradisea*
Family	Estrildidae or Ploceidae; sometimes included in Passeridae
Size	Male about 38cm (15in) long, including tail; female much smaller
Distribution	Eastern and southern Africa, from Sudan to Angola and South Africa
Habitat	Semi-arid open scrub, savannah and thorn-bush country
Diet	Mainly seeds
Breeding	Polygynous. Brood parasite: female lays eggs in nests of other birds, usually melba waxbill (*Pytilia melba*), which incubates and raises young

Red bishop

The true weavers of the family Ploceidae are named for the wonderfully intricate nests they build. These are literally woven from fine grass and reed leaves, and suspended from a tree or, in the case of bishops and some other species, attached to reed, bulrush or sugarcane stems a metre or two (3–6ft) above the ground or water. The nest is generally globe-shaped, with an entrance underneath and a separate egg-chamber inside. Only male red bishops during the breeding season have the colourful plumage illustrated; females and non-breeding males are buff and brown. Males build several nests in their territory, each for one of his three or four mates.

Scientific name	*Euplectes* (or *Pyromelana*) *orix*
Family	Ploceidae; sometimes included in Passeridae
Size	13–14cm (5–5½in) long
Distribution	Sub-Saharan Africa, from Kenya to Angola and South Africa
Habitat	Open savannah grassland, often near water
Diet	Seeds (mainly grains and grasses); insects
Breeding	Polygynous. Male weaves oval nests of grass and reed leaves, attached to reed or similar stems; three eggs, incubated by female for 11–14 days

Sociable weaver

The sociable (or social) weaver belongs to a group of birds known as sparrow-weavers, which may be classified as either weavers or sparrows – one reason for grouping all these related birds in one big family (*see p.288*). It is a sparrow-like bird that feeds on the ground and is renowned for building huge communal nests. The birds start by building a communal thatched roof of straw and twigs, usually in an acacia tree; individual pairs then weave individual flask-shaped nest chambers, entered from below. The nest may be added to over the years, eventually reaching 6m (20ft) across, weighing up to a tonne, and accommodating more than 100 pairs.

Scientific name	*Philetarius socius*
Family	Ploceidae or Passeridae
Size	About 14cm (5½in) long
Distribution	South Africa and Namibia
Habitat	Semi-arid scrubland
Diet	Seeds; insects
Breeding	Huge communal nest, housing many pairs in separate chambers, in tree (*see above*); three or four eggs (incubation period uncertain)

Sudan golden sparrow

In a family of mostly rather dull, brownish birds, the Sudan golden sparrow is outstandingly colourful – at least in the male, which is a golden to pale lemon-yellow colour with a chestnut-brown back and shoulders, and a bill that becomes markedly blacker in the breeding season. The female is a much more drab buff-brown, with just a hint of yellow on the face. The birds' attractiveness makes them a popular, although not very common, caged pet. Caged-bird breeders sometimes call them golden song sparrows, but this rather overstates their vocal skill: Their 'song' is a chirping rather like a much louder version of the house sparrow's (see p.292).

Scientific name	*Passer luteus*
Family	Passeridae, or sometimes placed in Ploceidae
Size	12–13cm (4½–5in) long
Distribution	Sahel region across sub-Saharan Africa; south-eastern Egypt
Habitat	Dry savannah and semi-desert, often near cultivated land
Diet	Mainly seeds; some insects (especially to feed young)
Breeding	Bulky nest of twigs and other materials in tree or bush; two to four eggs, incubated for about 12 days

House sparrow

No bird, even the feral pigeon (*see p.134*), is more closely associated with people than the house sparrow. It originated as a seed-eater in Europe, North Africa and western Asia, and was given the name *passer* (now its scientific name) by the Romans. Introduced populations are now established on every continent except Antarctica, although numbers dropped drastically in Britain, for unknown reasons, in the late 20th century. Only in eastern Asia does the similar Eurasian tree sparrow (*P. montanus*) largely take its place. The house sparrow is a noisy, gregarious bird whose success is due to its ability to eat almost anything and nest almost anywhere.

Scientific name	*Passer domesticus*
Family	Passeridae, or sometimes placed in Ploceidae
Size	About 15cm (6in) long
Distribution	Originally Eurasia, North Africa and Middle East; introduced widely
Habitat	Most open habitats, but especially farmland, parks and gardens
Diet	Almost anything: seeds; fruits; insects; worms; refuse; kitchen scraps
Breeding	Untidy nest of grass, twigs and other material in crevice in wall, building or tree; three to five eggs, incubated mainly by female for 11–14 days

White-winged snowfinch

A hardy and bold little bird, the snowfinch is not afraid to scrounge scraps of bread and other food from visitors to alpine resorts. In bad winter weather it may be forced down into sheltered valleys, but at other times it inhabits high-altitude meadows, screes and barren, rocky slopes. It walks quickly on the ground foraging for seeds and insects. It looks rather like a pale-coloured house sparrow (*see opposite*), with a large white patch on each wing that shows conspicuously in flight. The male has a grey head, while the female's is brownish. Both sexes have a black bill during the breeding season, but this fades to a yellowish colour in winter.

Scientific name	*Montifringilla nivalis*
Family	Passeridae, or sometimes placed in Ploceidae
Size	17–18cm (6½–7in) long
Distribution	Isolated mountainous areas from southern Europe to Himalayas
Habitat	Alpine meadows and rocky slopes, at 1400–5000m (4500–16 000ft)
Diet	Seeds; insects
Breeding	Nest of grass, moss and feathers in rock crevice, wall or burrow; four or five eggs, incubated by both sexes for 13–14 days

Common or Eurasian starling

Starlings are well-known birds of cities, towns and the countryside that originated in the Eurasian and Mediterranean area but have been introduced as far afield as North America, South Africa and south-eastern Australia. They are handsome birds, with iridescent purple, green and blue plumage speckled with white or buff, but they are not widely loved. They are strutting, pugnacious and noisy, forming huge wheeling flocks as they roost at dusk on trees and buildings, and are blamed for fouling buildings and streets, for harming trees and for damaging crops. Yet in many regions they are welcomed as destroyers of huge numbers of insect pests.

Scientific name	*Sturnus vulgaris*
Family	Sturnidae
Size	20–23cm (8–9in) long
Distribution	Europe; North Africa; western and southern Asia; introduced elsewhere
Habitat	Most habitats, especially near farmland and human settlements
Diet	Worms; insects and larvae; other invertebrates; fruits; berries; seeds
Breeding	Cup-shaped nest of plant materials in hole in tree, in rock crevice or in building; up to seven eggs, incubated by both sexes for 12–13 days

Hill mynah

Renowned as the best of all birds at mimicking the human voice, hill mynahs chatter noisily in the wild and utter a wide variety of calls – some musical, some harsh – as they feed among the forest trees. They do not mimic other species in the wild, but a family or larger group of paired birds (which mate for life) do mimic each other, so that each group has a slightly different vocabulary of calls. This is the origin of their mimicry of people, which is far more accurate than that of parrots and which develops best if the birds have human company from a young age. The related common or Indian mynah (*Acridotheres tristis*) is not such a good mimic.

Scientific name	*Gracula religiosa*
Family	Sturnidae
Size	Populations vary from 30–38cm (12–15in) long
Distribution	India, Sri Lanka and southern China to south-east Asia and Indonesia
Habitat	Forests and woodland
Diet	Wild figs and other fruits; berries; buds; some insects and lizards; nectar
Breeding	Pairs for life. Cup-shaped nest in hole (often old woodpecker hole) in tree; two or three eggs, incubated by both sexes for 14–15 days

Golden oriole

In spite of the male's yellow body (the female is greenish), these shy and secretive birds are hard to spot as they search for food in the tree tops. Golden orioles like tall deciduous woodland with an open canopy. They rarely come to ground, flying swiftly in shallow swoops and even taking a bath by fluttering their wings to spray water on themselves briefly before returning to their cover. The golden oriole is one of about 25 species of true or Old World orioles, many yellow in colour and all but one – the green figbird (*Sphecotheres viridis*) – belonging to the genus *Oriolus*. They are not related to the outwardly similar New World orioles (*see p.278*).

Scientific name	*Oriolus oriolus*
Family	Oriolidae
Size	23–25cm (8–9in) long
Distribution	Much of Europe, central Asia and North Africa; winters in Africa, India
Habitat	Deciduous woodland; orchards; parks; savannah
Diet	Fruits; insects
Breeding	Hammock-like cup-shaped nest of plant and other materials, on forked branch; three or four eggs, incubated mainly by female for 14–15 days

Greater racket-tailed drongo

Elongated outer tail feathers – slightly shorter in females – each ending in a flag-like 'racket', together with a prominent head-crest, distinguish this large species of drongo. All drongos are highly territorial forest birds that defend their own areas furiously, even against large birds of prey such as eagles. Their aggression pervades their entire lifestyle; they flush insects out of the trees and hunt them on the wing, like flycatchers (*see p.257*) but with a definite ferocity. Such is their aggression that the tree where a drongo nests is likely to be inhabited by several other, less forceful bird species that gain protection – so long as they are left in peace by the drongo.

Scientific name	*Dicrurus parsadiseus*
Family	Dicruridae
Size	About 65cm (26in) long, including tail feathers; female slightly shorter
Distribution	Himalayas and south-western China south to Sri Lanka and Indonesia
Habitat	Forests; bamboo thickets; edges of cultivated land
Diet	Insects (mainly flying) and larvae; some lizards and small birds
Breeding	Loose cup-shaped nest on high, forked branch of tree; usually two or three eggs, believed incubated mainly by female (period uncertain)

Streaked bowerbird

Male bowerbirds are incredibly skilled builders, making elaborate 'bowers' to lure females. These are not nests, and after mating (in the bower) females build the nest, incubate the eggs and raise the young; males often mate again. As a rule, dull-coloured species make the most elaborate bowers. Streaked bowerbirds, or orange-crested gardeners, are 'maypole builders'. They pile sticks around a small tree-trunk to make a pyramid 1.5m (5ft) or more tall, then a smaller pyramid nearby. They roof over the space in between to make the bower, decorating it with ferns, mosses and flowers, which are renewed as they fade – hence the name 'gardener'.

Scientific name	*Amblyornis subalaris*
Family	Ptilonorhynchidae; sometimes formerly included in Paradisaeidae
Size	About 23cm (9in) long
Distribution	South-east New Guinea
Habitat	Humid montane rainforest at 600–1500m (2000–5000ft)
Diet	Mainly forest fruits; some insects
Breeding	Probably polygynous. After mating (*see above*), female builds cup-shaped nest; usually two eggs, incubated by female for about 21 days

Satin bowerbird

This species is one of the group of bowerbirds known as 'avenue builders'. Its bower is much smaller than that of the maypole builders (*see opposite*) but is elaborately decorated. It consists of a pair of parallel walls, about 30cm (12in) tall and 15cm (6in) apart, into which the female is lured for mating. It is made of woven sticks planted into the ground in a well-trodden, cleared space. The male paints the bower's inner surfaces with a mixture of saliva with charcoal and other pigments, using a wad of bark as a 'paintbrush'. He also decorates it with colourful – bright blue is the favourite – feathers, pebbles, shells, flowers and even scraps of plastic.

Scientific name	*Ptilonorhynchus violaceus*
Family	Ptilonorhynchidae; sometimes formerly included in Paradisaeidae
Size	27–33cm (10½–13in) long
Distribution	Australia east of Great Dividing Range
Habitat	Temperate and tropical rainforest; sclerophyll forest edges
Diet	Fruits; leaves; insects
Breeding	Polygynous. After mating (*see above*), female builds cup-shaped nest in tree; usually two blotched eggs, incubated by female for about 21 days

King bird of paradise

Birds of paradise were once thought to be closely related to the bowerbirds (*see pp.298–299*), which inhabit similar territories and were sometimes placed in the same family. However, DNA evidence shows that they are unrelated; in fact birds of paradise's closest relatives are crows. Males use colourful or extravagant plumage to entice females. The king bird of paradise is the smallest member of the family and one of the most brilliantly coloured, with a scarlet back, blue feet and wiry tail feathers ending in metallic-green round plumes. The female, in contrast, is a dull olive-brown, without tail plumes. After mating, she undertakes all nesting duties.

Scientific name	*Cicinnurus regius*
Family	Paradisaeidae
Size	Male about 30cm (12in) long, including tail; female about 18cm (7in)
Distribution	Parts of New Guinea and some offshore islands
Habitat	Lowland rainforest
Diet	Mainly small fruits and berries; some insects
Breeding	Polygynous. Cup-shaped nest of palm fibres, made in hole in tree by female; usually two eggs, incubated by female for about 12 days

Lawes's parotia

Members of the genus *Parotia* are sometimes called six-wired birds of paradise because the males have three wire-like feathers growing from each side of the head, each of them ending in a small black plume or 'racket'. Male Lawes's parotias are less colourful than most birds of paradise – they are all black apart from their iridescent bib – but they have a magnificent ruff of soft black plumes covering their breast. Males of this species compete with each other for females in a common display area, or lek, prancing and displaying their finery before a group of females, who choose their mate. A successful, dominant male may mate with many females.

Scientific name	*Parotia lawesii*
Family	Paradisaeidae
Size	About 25cm (10in) long
Distribution	South-eastern New Guinea
Habitat	Montane rainforest at 1200–1900m (4000–6250ft)
Diet	Mainly fruits and berries; some insects and other invertebrates
Breeding	Polygynous. Female builds bulky cup-shaped nest of twigs and other materials; usually two eggs, incubated by female for about 19 days

Greater bird of paradise

The first specimens of birds of paradise to reach Europe in the 16th century were simply skins – with feathers but with the feet removed – prepared by native New Guinea people. This gave rise to the myth that these birds spend their entire life on the wing, like angels, falling to earth only when they die. By the time the Swedish naturalist Carolus Linnaeus named the greater bird of paradise in the 18th century, complete specimens, with feet, were known, but Linnaeus referred to the old myth by giving it the species name *apoda* ('without feet'). It has among the most beautiful plumage of all, which groups of males display to females on the branches of a tree.

Scientific name	*Paradisaea apoda*
Family	Paradisaeidae
Size	Male about 43cm (17in) long; female 35cm (14in)
Distribution	South-eastern New Guinea
Habitat	Lowland rainforest, to 950m (3000ft)
Diet	Fruits and berries; probably some insects
Breeding	Polygynous. Female builds cup-shaped nest of twigs and other plant materials; usually two eggs, incubated by female for about 17–23 days

Emperor bird of paradise

The names of many birds of paradise either include a superlative such as 'superb' or 'magnificent', or refer to a ruler whom their discoverer wanted to honour. The emperor referred to in the case of this species was Wilhelm (or William) II, who became Kaiser (emperor) of Germany in 1888, a few years after north-east New Guinea was made a German colony. The species name *guilielmi* comes from the Latin version of William. It is a beautiful bird, rather similar to the greater bird of paradise (*opposite*), with a green crown and breast in males. These also make group displays to females, involving hanging upside-down from the branches of a tree.

Scientific name	*Paradisaea guilielmi*
Family	Paradisaeidae
Size	Male about 33cm (13in) long; female 31cm (12in)
Distribution	Small area of north-eastern New Guinea
Habitat	Mid-altitude rainforest, at 450–1500m (1500–5000ft)
Diet	Fruits and berries; probably some insects
Breeding	Polygynous. Female builds cup-shaped nest of twigs and other plant materials; usually two eggs, incubated by female for about 17–23 days

Superb bird of paradise

Mature males of this species, like the king bird of paradise (*see p.300*), defend their territory – and particularly their courtship area – against all other males. Each mature male has his own traditional display court, in a cleared area of forest. There he performs his courtship rituals, displaying his blue wedge-shaped breast shield and black cape, and dancing for the drab, brownish females. Females who accept the male's enticement mate with him and then perform all nesting duties alone while he mates with other females. Immature males – which look rather like females – have to wait many years to 'inherit' a display court, and may never do so.

Scientific name	*Lophorina superba*
Family	Paradisaeidae
Size	Male and female both about 24–25cm (9½–10in) long
Distribution	New Guinea
Habitat	Montane rainforest at 1650–1900m (5400–6250ft)
Diet	Insects and other invertebrates; small lizards; some fruits
Breeding	Polygynous. Female builds cup-shaped nest of twigs and other plant
	materials; usually two eggs, incubated by female for about 17–23 days

Magnificent riflebird

This bird's name comes from its call, a series of two to four explosive whistles, the last of which is deeper and more abrupt than the others. It is one of only a few birds of paradise that extend into northern Australia. It is territorial, like the superb bird of paradise (*opposite*), and the male holds and defends a display territory or court – in this case, high in a forest tree. In one display, he throws his head back to show his brillant blue throat and extends his wings. Their polygynous habits have protected birds of paradise from extinction by hunters – who are only interested in mature males, leaving immature birds to reach maturity and breed with females.

Scientific name	*Ptiloris magnificus*
Family	Paradisaeidae
Size	Male about 30–33cm (12–13in) long; female 25–28cm (10–11in)
Distribution	New Guinea; extreme north-eastern Australia
Habitat	Canopy of lowland to mid-altitude rainforest, up to 1400m (4600ft)
Diet	Fruits and berries; insects
Breeding	Polygynous. Female builds loose cup-shaped nest of leaves and other materials; usually two eggs, incubated by female for about 15–16 days

Eurasian jay

Despite variations over its wide geographical range, the common Eurasian jay's colouring is unmistakable: a brownish to clear pink body, bright blue wing bars and a black 'moustache'. Its loud, harsh cries are, however, more likely to be heard than the bird is to be seen, for it is cautious and keeps to the shelter of trees more than other members of the crow family living in its range. It may be seen in parks and gardens, but it does not stray very far from shelter. When it is seen, it is usually as solitary birds or pairs as they forage on the ground and in trees for their very varied food. Where oak trees grow they are particularly fond of acorns, which they bury, squirrel-fashion, to retrieve and eat in winter.

Scientific name	*Garrulus glandarius*
Family	Corvidae
Size	33–35cm (13–14in) long
Distribution	Europe; western North Africa; central, eastern and south-eastern Asia
Habitat	Deciduous and mixed forests; woodland; parks; gardens with trees
Diet	Acorns; seeds; fruits; insects and larvae; worms; eggs; small mammals
Breeding	Cup-shaped nest of twigs and other materials, in tree; usually three to six eggs, incubated by female (fed by male) for 16–19 days

Turquoise jay

The jays include many of the most beautiful members of the crow family. None are more colourful than those of Central and South America, where almost 30 species of New World jays are found. The exquisite turquoise jay – almost entirely an intense turquoise-blue except for black markings on its face, a grey-black bill, and black legs and feet – is found high in the Andes of South America. Its range centres on Ecuador but extends into parts of neighbouring Colombia and Peru. At the altitude of around 2000m (6500ft) where it lives, the forest is shrouded in cloud for much of the time, and epiphytic ('air') plants without roots drape the trees. Turquoise jays are quite common there, feeding in noisy groups.

Scientific name	*Cyanolyca turcosa*
Family	Corvidae
Size	About 33cm (13in) long
Distribution	Andes of southern Colombia, Ecuador and northern Peru
Habitat	Humid montane forest (cloud forest), at 2000–3000m (6500–10 000ft)
Diet	Mainly insects; some fruits
Breeding	Information not known

PASSERIFORMES (PERCHING BIRDS)

Pander's or Turkestan ground jay

Ground jays, as their name suggests, are mostly terrestrial birds that are very poor fliers. They are quite small but long-legged birds that run well and also hop, but rarely fly. Pander's ground jay, also known as the Turkestan ground jay or saxaul jay, lives in the Central Asian southern desert area, including the Kara Kum and Kyzyl Kum sandy deserts. It is a handsome bird that is well camouflaged by its colouring. Helped by its wings, it is said to run faster than any other bird of its size. It feeds mainly on insects and small lizards, but may resort to seeds and buds in winter when animal food is scarce. It gets all the water it needs from its insect prey.

Scientific name	*Podoces panderi*
Family	Corvidae
Size	20–25cm (8–10in) long
Distribution	South-central Asia: Kazakhstan, Uzbekistan, Turkmenistan, Kyrgyzstan
Habitat	Sandy desert and semi-arid scrubland
Diet	Mainly insects and small lizards; seeds and buds in winter
Breeding	Builds cup-shaped nest at base of bush; said also to nest in burrows; other details of breeding uncertain

Common or black-billed magpie

Magpies are renowned for stealing brightly coloured and shiny objects. However, it is for the birds' much exaggerated reputation as nest robbers – of game bird nests in particular – that gamekeepers hate them. Yet in some country areas of Britain they are supposed to bring good luck if they are greeted politely. Originally a woodland species, the common magpie (known in North America as the black-billed magpie) has expanded into farmland and towns. It has short wings and is not a strong flier, but its long tail enables it to manoeuvre with considerable agility. It is a sociable bird outside the breeding season, when large groups may gather in trees, chattering and chasing each other.

Scientific name	*Pica pica*
Family	Corvidae
Size	43–48cm (17–19in) long, including tail
Distribution	Europe; Asia except south and far north; north-western North America
Habitat	Woodland; farmland and open country with trees; parks; gardens
Diet	Insects; snails; other invertebrates; seeds; small mammals and birds
Breeding	Bowl-shaped domed nest of twigs, mud and other materials, in bush or tree; five to eight eggs, incubated by female for 17–18 days

Ceylon blue magpie

Often called simply the Ceylon magpie, this beautiful, glossy blue and chestnut-brown bird is a rather shy rainforest species. Much of Sri Lanka's forests have been felled for agriculture and fuel, and the Ceylon magpie is threatened by this habitat destruction, but it survives in good numbers in areas where the forest is protected. There it is usually seen in small groups of six to eight birds, or sometimes as pairs or solitary individuals. It is agile and energetic, and spends most of its time searching the trees' foliage – at all levels from the forest floor to the canopy – for food, often hanging upside-down. It is a noisy bird, especially in the rainy season, making a variety of ringing or cheeping calls.

Scientific name	*Urocissa* (or *Cissa*) *ornata*
Family	Corvidae
Size	45–50cm (18–20in) long
Distribution	South-western Sri Lanka
Habitat	Lowland and mountain rainforest; occasionally in plantations
Diet	Insects and larvae (including hairy caterpillars); tree-frogs and lizards
Breeding	Nest of twigs, well concealed among foliage high in jungle tree; three to five spotted and speckled eggs (incubation period uncertain)

Eurasian jackdaw

In a family of thieves, the jackdaw is perhaps the greatest offender. It robs other birds of eggs and chicks, robs horses and sheep of tufts of hair for nest-building, and may even take lodging in part of a rook's nest. Like the magpie (*see p.309*), it steals and hides inedible objects. But it is also sociable and intelligent, with a highly structured family life. Jackdaws mate for life, and live and breed in colonies that have a well developed social 'pecking order'. They have an elaborate courtship ritual, in which the male bows and spreads his wings. Above all, they have taken advantage of human activities that have increased food supplies and nesting sites.

Scientific name	*Corvus monedula*
Family	Corvidae
Size	About 33cm (13in) long
Distribution	Europe; western and central Asia; western North Africa; some migrate
Habitat	Mountains and cliffs; woodland; parks; towns and cities
Diet	Worms, insects and other invertebrates; seeds; fruit; eggs; carrion
Breeding	Cup-shaped nest of sticks and other plant materials, in hole in tree, cliff or building; three to six blue eggs, incubated by female for 16–20 days

Common raven

Ravens are the biggest members of the crow family and the biggest-bodied of all perching birds; the biggest species is the east African thick-billed raven (*Corvus crassirostris*). Common ravens have long been persecuted for killing farm stock; in fact they behave like vultures, following predatory mammals for scraps and soaring over grazing country looking for dead or sickly prey. They also eat almost anything from fish and insects to acorns and fruit. At one time they scavenged in city streets, but most have been driven out into wilder country. They are long-lived birds, and have been regarded as omens – for good or ill – since at least Roman times.

Scientific name	*Corvus corax*
Family	Corvidae
Size	60–66cm (23½–26in) long
Distribution	Europe; Asia (except south, south-east); North Africa; North America
Habitat	Mountains; sea cliffs; wasteland; elsewhere with suitable nest sites
Diet	Mainly small animals and carrion; also seeds, fruit, eggs, nestling birds
Breeding	Large nest of sticks, moss and mud, in crevice, on ledge or in tall tree;
	four to six pale blue or green eggs, incubated by female for 19–20 days

Clark's nutcracker

Nutcrackers are so called because they have a long, sharp, strong bill for prising the seeds (or 'nuts') from pine cones and (using a special projection inside the lower mandible) cracking them open. They also have a special throat pouch for transporting the seeds without swallowing them. Clark's nutcracker is named after Willam Clark, who discovered the bird during his expedition across the Rocky Mountains with Meriweather Lewis in 1804–06. It is renowned for storing pine seeds – one bird may bury 30 000 seeds in a season, in thousands of small caches – and being able to find them later from memory and dig them up, even when covered by snow.

Scientific name	*Nucifraga columbiana*
Family	Corvidae
Size	28–33cm (11–13in) long
Distribution	Western North America, from British Columbia to New Mexico
Habitat	Open coniferous forests and clearings at high altitudes; valleys in winter
Diet	Mainly conifer (especially pine) seeds; other seeds; nuts; berries; insects
Breeding	Nest of twigs and other plant materials, on outer branch of conifer tree; two to four pale green eggs, incubated by both sexes for 16–18 days

Index